Exclusive Distributors:
**Music Sales Limited**
8/9 Frith Street,
London W1D 3JB, England.
**Music Sales Pty Limited**
120 Rothschild Avenue,
Rosebery, NSW 2018,
Australia.

Order No. AM966680
ISBN 0-7119-8417-4
This book © Copyright 2000 by Wise Publications

Compiled by Paul Honey, Jack Long and Nick Crispin
Music arrangements by Paul Honey and Jack Long
Music processed by Enigma Music Production Services

CDs performed and recorded by Paul Honey

**Your Guarantee of Quality**
As publishers, we strive to produce every book
to the highest commercial standards.
This book has been carefully designed to minimise awkward
page turns and to make playing from it a real pleasure.
Particular care has been given to specifying acid-free,
neutral-sized paper made from pulps which have not been
elemental chlorine bleached. This pulp is from farmed sustainable
forests and was produced with special regard for the environment.
Throughout, the printing and binding have been planned to ensure a
sturdy, attractive publication which should give years of enjoyment.
If your copy fails to meet our high standards, please inform us and
we will gladly replace it.

Music Sales' complete catalogue describes thousands of
titles and is available in full colour sections by subject, direct
from Music Sales Limited. Please state your areas of interest and
send a cheque/postal order for £1.50 for postage to:
Music Sales Limited, Newmarket Road, Bury St. Edmunds,
Suffolk IP33 3YB.

**www.musicsales.com**

## CD TRACKS

### Disc 1

1. Another Suitcase In Another Hall (Lloyd Webber/Rice) Evita Music Ltd.
2. Adelaide's Lament (Loesser) MPL Communications Ltd.
3. As Long As He Needs Me (Bart) Lakeview Music Publishing Co. Ltd.
4. Big Spender (Fields/Coleman) Campbell Connelly & Co. Ltd.
5. Can't Help Lovin' Dat Man (Kern/Hammerstein II) Universal Music Publishing Ltd.
6. Constant Craving (lang/Mink) Universal Music Publishing Ltd./Rondor Music (London) Ltd.
7. Crazy (Nelson) Acuff-Rose Music Ltd.
8. Don't Cry For Me Argentina (Lloyd Webber/Rice) Evita Music Ltd.
9. Diamonds Are A Girl's Best Friend (Robin/Styne) Dorsey Brothers Music Ltd.
10. Feeling Good (Bricusse/Newley) Concord Music Ltd.
11. Heaven Help My Heart (Andersson/Rice/Ulvaeus) Universal Music Publishing International Ltd.
12. I Cain't Say No (Rodgers/Hammerstein II) Williamson Music Ltd.
13. I Don't Know How To Love Him (Lloyd Webber/Rice) Universal/MCA Music Ltd.
14. I Dreamed A Dream (Schönberg/Kretzmer/Boublil/Natel) Alain Boublil Music Ltd., USA
15. I Say A Little Prayer (Bacharach/David) Universal/MCA Music Ltd./Windswept Pacific Music Ltd.
16. I Will Survive (Fekaris/Perren) Universal Music Publishing Ltd.
17. If I Were A Bell (Loesser) MPL Communications Ltd.
18. If My Friends Could See Me Now (Fields/Coleman) Campbell Connelly & Co. Ltd.
19. It's Oh So Quiet (Lang/Reisfeld/Meder) Peermusic (UK) Ltd.

### Disc 2

1. Memory (Lloyd Webber/Nunn/Eliot) The Really Useful Group Ltd./Faber Music Ltd.
2. Miss Byrd (Maltby Jr./Shire) Warner Chappell Music Ltd.
3. Killing Me Softly With His Song (Gimbel/Fox) Onward Music Ltd.
4. Now That I've Seen Her (Her Or Me) (Schönberg/Maltby Jr./Boublil) Alain Boublil Music Ltd., USA
5. Out Here On My Own (M. Gore/L. Gore) EMI United Partnership Ltd.
6. The Reason (King/Hudson/Wells) Universal/MCA Music Ltd./Rondor Music (London) Ltd./Bugle Songs Ltd.
7. Save The Best For Last (Lind/Waldman/Galdston) EMI Music Publishing (WP) Ltd./Universal Music Publishing Ltd./EMI Virgin Music Ltd.
8. Saving All My Love For You (Goffin/Masser) Chelsea Music Publishing Co. Ltd./Screen Gems-EMI Music Ltd.
9. Show Me Heaven (McKee/Rifkin/Rackin) Famous Music Corporation/Ensign Music Corporation, USA
10. Someone To Watch Over Me (G. Gershwin/I. Gershwin) Warner Chappell Music Ltd.
11. Tell Me It's Not True (Russell) Timeact Ltd.
12. That Ole Devil Called Love (Fisher/Roberts) Universal/MCA Music Ltd.
13. What I Did For Love (Kleban/Hamlisch) Chappell Morris Ltd./BMG Music Publishing Ltd.
14. Someone Else's Story (Andersson/Rice/Ulvaeus) Universal Music Publishing International Ltd.
15. The Wind Beneath My Wings (Silbar/Henley) Warner Chappell Music Ltd.
16. The Winner Takes It All (Andersson/Ulvaeus) Bocu Music Ltd.
17. Wishing You Were Somehow Here Again (Lloyd Webber/Hart/Stilgoe) The Really Useful Group Ltd.
18. You Can Always Count On Me (Zippel/Coleman) Warner Chappell Music Ltd.
19. You Must Love Me (Lloyd Webber/Rice) Evita Music Ltd.

# Professional Singers Audition Book

1 CD MISSING

London/New York/Sydney/Copenhagen/Madrid/Tokyo

# Disc 1

# Another Suitcase In Another Hall

Music by Andrew Lloyd Webber
Lyrics by Tim Rice

1. I don't ex-pect my love af-fairs to last for long Nev-er
*(Verses 2 & 3 see block lyric)*
fool my-self that my dreams will come true. Be-ing used to trou-ble I an-

- ti - ci-pate_ it; But all the same_ I hate it, Would-n't you? So what hap-pens

now? So what hap-pens now?\_\_\_\_\_ Where am I go-ing to?

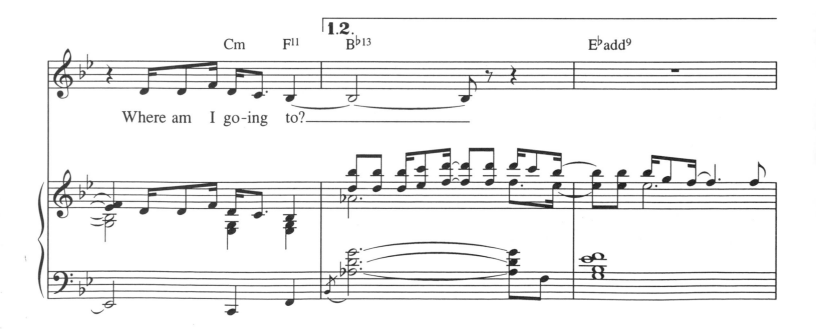

Where am I go-ing to?\_\_\_\_\_

*Verse 2*

Time and time again I've said that I don't care,
That I'm immune to gloom, that I'm hard through and through.
But, every time it matters, all my words desert me;
So anyone can hurt me – and they do!
So what happens now? etc.

*Verse 3*

Call in three months' time and I'll be fine, I know;
Well maybe not that fine, but I'll survive anyhow.
I won't recall the names and faces of this sad occasion;
But that's no consolation here and now.
So what happens now? etc.

# Adelaide's Lament

## Words & Music by Frank Loesser

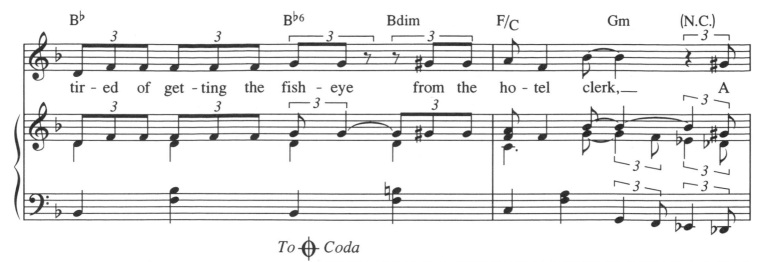

tir - ed of get -ting the fish - eye from the ho - tel clerk,— A

*To ⊕ Coda*

**1.**

F/C  C/G  C⁷  F

per - son can de-vel-op a cold.

**2.**  *D. 𝄋 al Coda*

F  C⁷

2. The cough. And

⊕ **CODA**

F  D⁷  Gm⁷  C⁷  F  Am/E

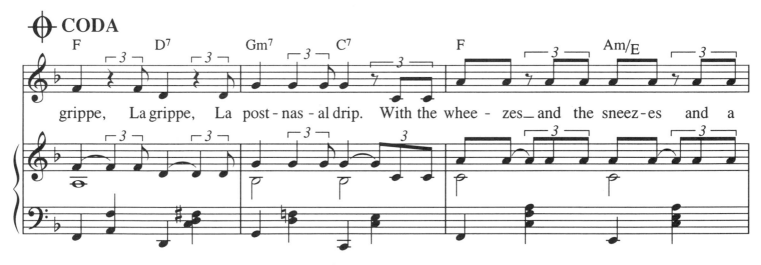

grippe, La grippe, La post - nas - al drip. With the whee - zes and the sneez-es and a

**Slower**

Am⁷⁽♭⁵⁾/E♭  D⁷aug  N.C.  B♭6  B♭m⁷

sin - us that's real - ly a pip! From a lack of com - mu - ni - ty pro - per - ty and a

feel-ing she's get-ting too old, A per-son___ can de-vel-op a bad bad

cold._____

*Verse 2*

The female remaining single, just in the legal sense,
Shows a neurotic tendency. See note. (Spoken) Note.
Chronic organic syndromes, toxic or hypertense,
Involving the eye, the ear, and the nose and the throat.
In other words, just from worrying whether the wedding is on or off,
A person can develop a cough!
You can feed her all day with the Vitamin A and the Bromo Fizz,
But the medicine never gets anywhere near where the trouble is.
If she's getting a kind of a name for herself, and the name ain't his,
A person can develop a cough!

*Verse 3*

And furthermore, just from stalling and stalling and stalling the wedding trip,
A person can develop La grippe!
When they get on the train for Niag'ra and she can hear church bells chime,
The compartment is air-conditioned and the mood sublime,
Then they get off at Saratoga for the fourteenth time,
A person can develop La grippe,
La grippe, La post-nasal drip, etc.

# As Long As He Needs Me

## Words & Music by Lionel Bart

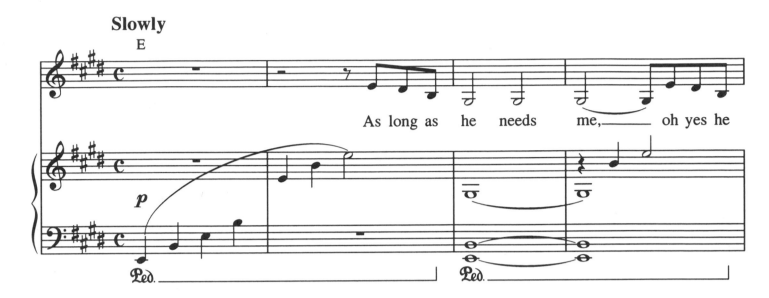

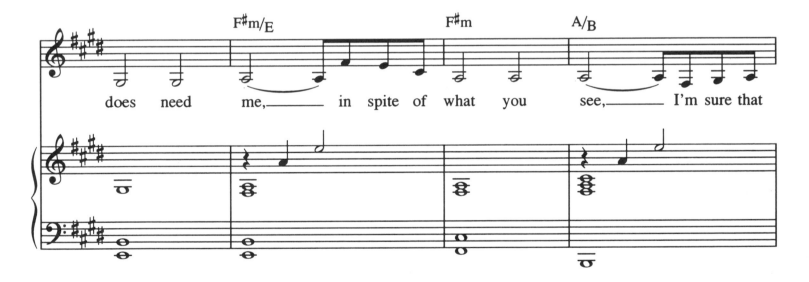

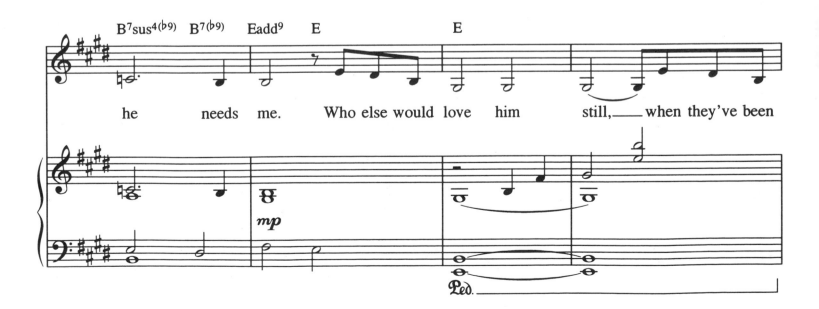

used so ill?_____ He knows I al - ways will,\_\_\_\_\_ as long as

he needs me. I miss him so much\_\_\_\_ when he is gone.

**Con moto**

But when he's near me,\_\_\_\_\_ I don't let on. The way I

**poco rall.**

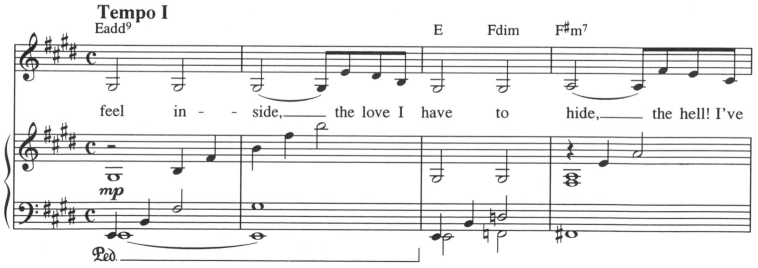

feel in - - side,\_\_\_\_ the love I have to hide,\_\_\_\_ the hell! I've

**Tempo I**

got my pride, _____ as long as he needs me.

**Con moto**

He does-n't say the things he should, he acts the way he thinks he should.

**rall.**

But all the same I'll play this game his way. _____

**a tempo**

— As long as he needs me, _____ I know where I must

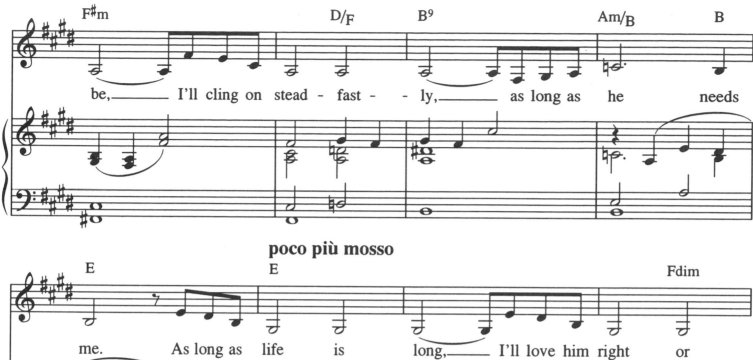

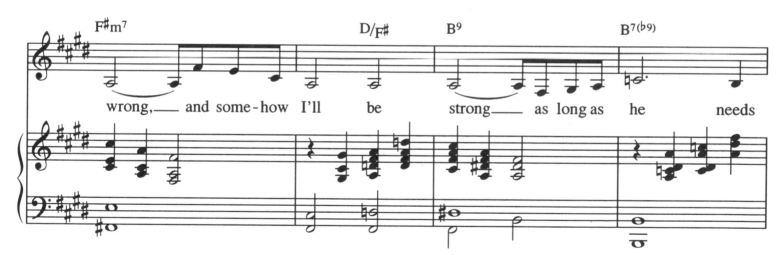

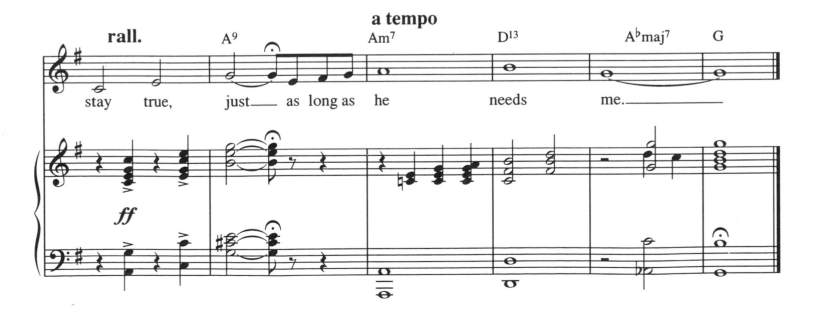

# Big Spender

Words by Dorothy Fields
Music by Cy Coleman

I don't pop my cork for ev'-ry guy I see.___

Hey! Big Spen-der,___ Spend a lit-tle time___ with

me. Would-n't you like to have

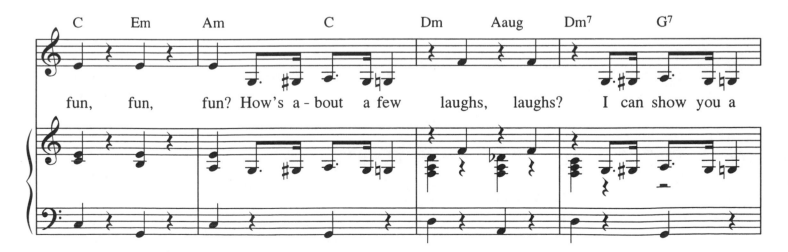

fun, fun, fun? How's a-bout a few laughs, laughs? I can show you a

good time,____ Let me show you a____ good time.____ The min-ute you

**CODA**

Hey, Big Spen-der____ Hey, Big Spen-der!____

Spend_____ a lit-tle time____ with me, Spend a lit-tle time____ with

me, Spend a lit-tle time____ with me.____

# Can't Help Lovin' Dat Man

Music by Jerome Kern
Words by Oscar Hammerstein II

Oh lis-ten sis-ter, I love my Mis-ter

man____ and I can't tell yo' why,___ Dere ain't no rea-son

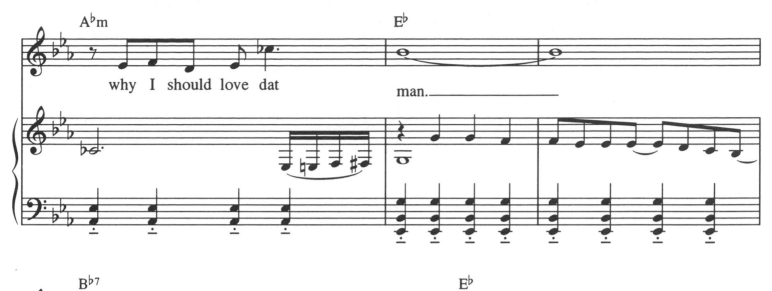

why I should love dat man.

It must be sump-in' dat__ de an-gels done plan.

Fish got to swim,__ birds got to fly,__ I got to love__ one

man till I die,__ Can't help lov-in' dat man__ of

21

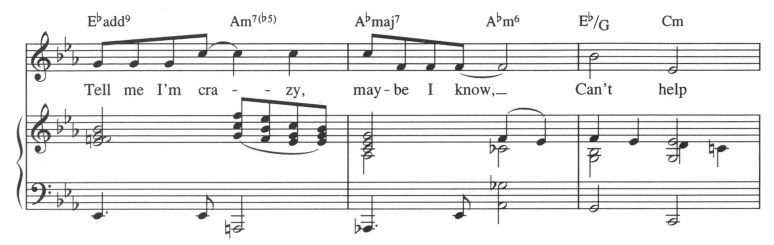

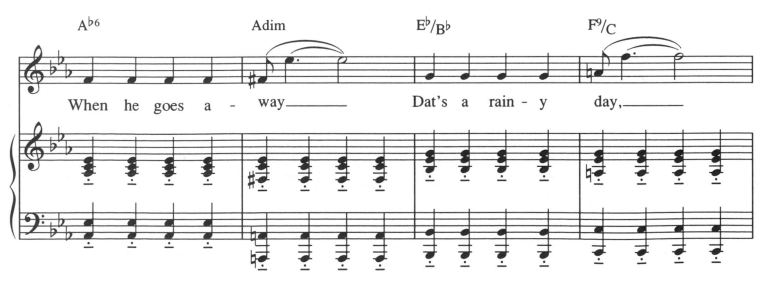

And when he comes back dat day is fine,_____ The sun will shine.

He can come home__ as late as can be,__ Home with-out him__ ain't

no home to me,__ Can't help lov-in' dat man__ of

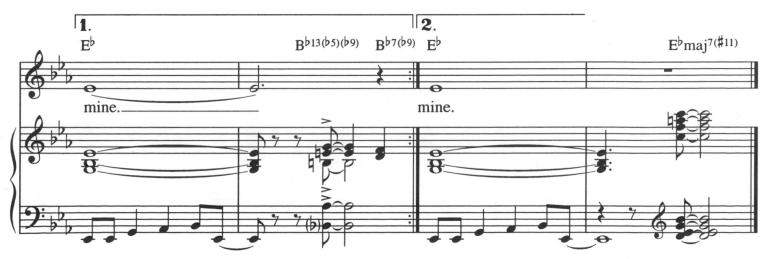

mine._____ mine.

# Constant Craving

Words & Music by k.d. lang & Ben Mink

**Medium rock**

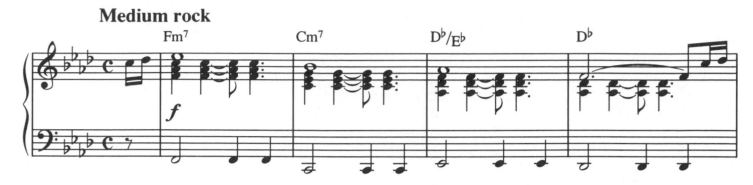

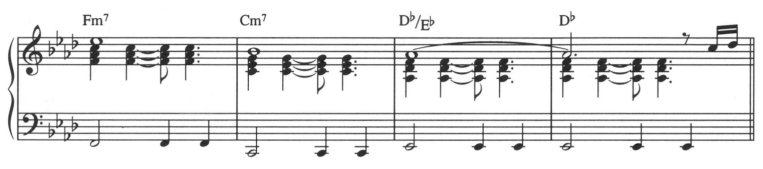

1. Ev - - en through the dark - est phase, be
*(Verse 2 see block lyric)*

it thick or thin._____ Al - - -

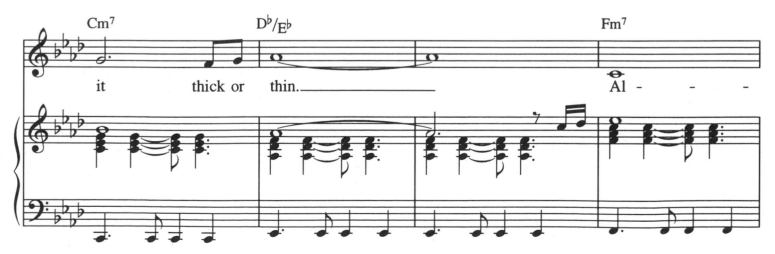

- ways some-one march - es brave, here be - neath my

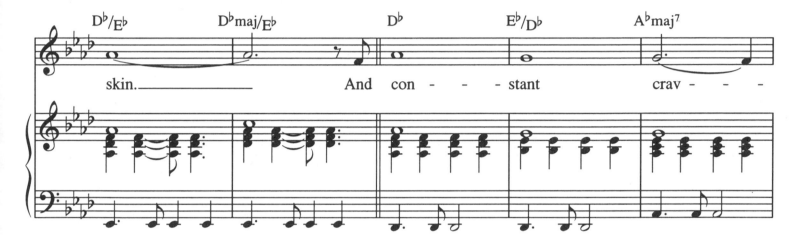

skin._____ And con - - stant crav - - -

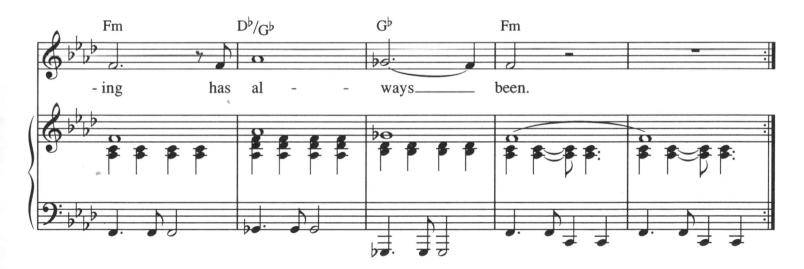

- ing has al - - ways_____ been.

Crav - - ing. Ah ha,_____ con-stant crav - -

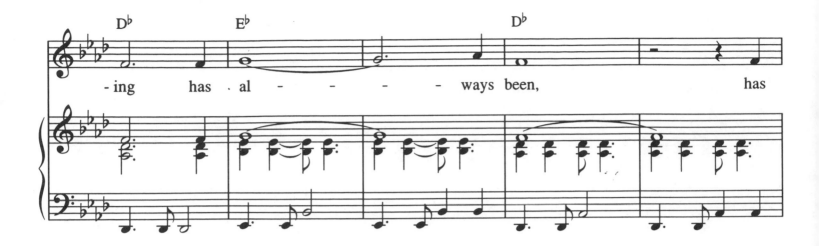

-ing has al - - - - ways been, has

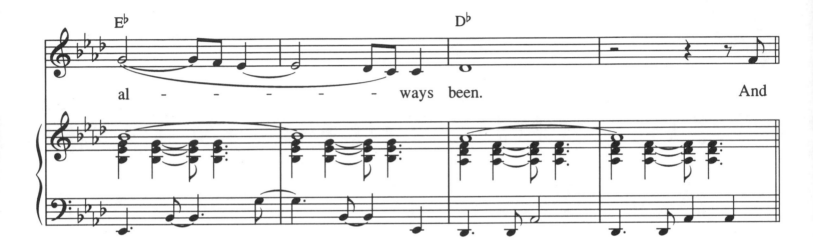

al - - - - ways been. And

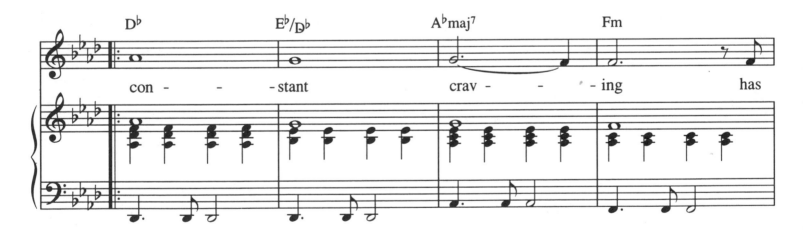

con - -stant crav - - -ing has

al - - ways_____ been.

*Verse 2:*
Maybe a great magnet pulls
All souls towards the truth.
Or maybe it is life itself,
That feeds wisdom to its youth.

# Crazy

## Words & Music by Willie Nelson

Cra - zy,___

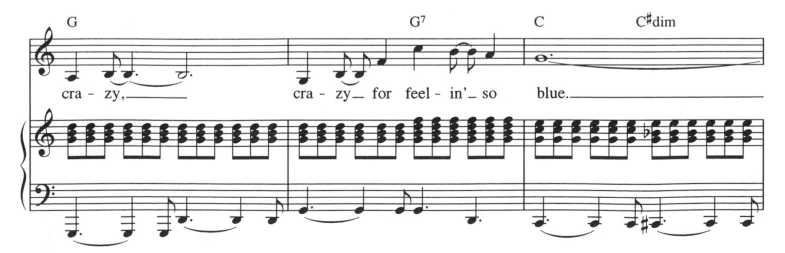

cra - zy_ for feel - in'_ so lone - ly,___ I'm

cra - zy,___ cra - zy_ for feel - in' so blue.___

I know_____ you'd love me_ as long as_ you

want - ed,_____ and then some - day_____ you'd

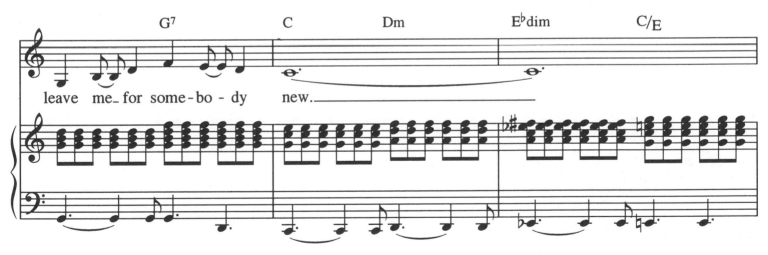

leave me_ for some - bo - dy new._____

Wor - ry,_____ why do_ I let my - self wor - ry?_____

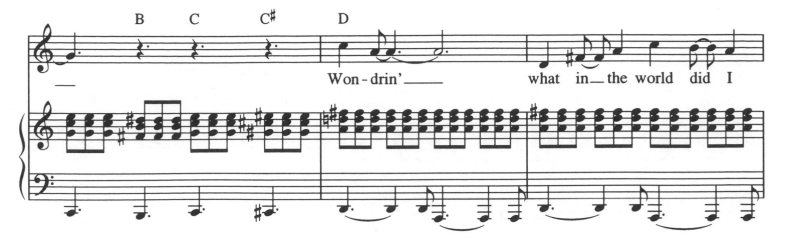

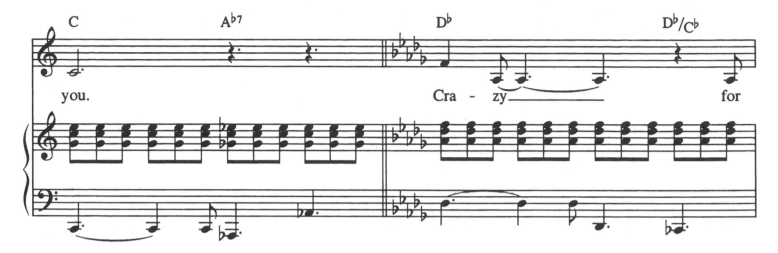

you.

Cra - zy_____ for

think - ing_ that my love_ could hold you._____

_ I'm cra - zy_ for try - in', cra - zy_ for cry - in'_ and I'm

cra - zy for lov - in' you.

# Don't Cry For Me Argentina

## Music by Andrew Lloyd Webber
## Lyrics by Tim Rice

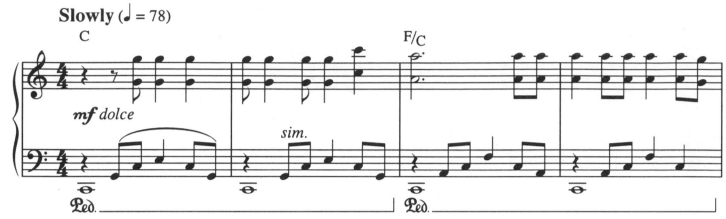

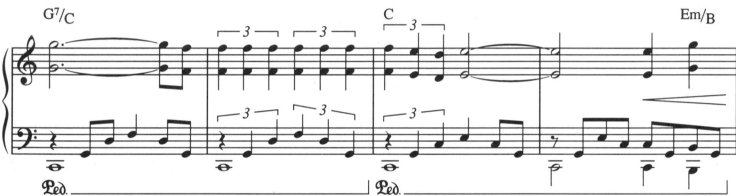

1. It won't be

ea-sy, you'll think it strange When I try to ex-plain how I feel, That I

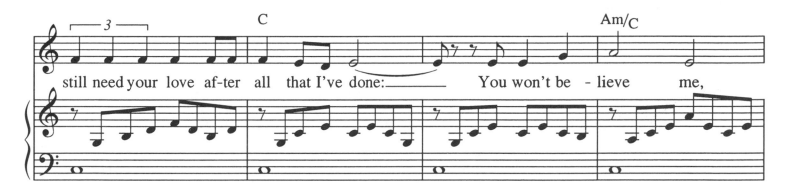

still need your love af-ter all that I've done:_____ You won't be - lieve me,

All you will see is a girl you once knew, Al - though she's dressed up to the

nines at six-es and se-vens with you. 2. I had to let it

hap-pen, I had to change; Could-n't stay all my life down at heel: Look-ing

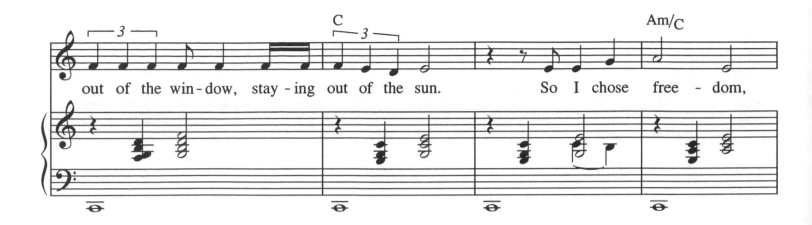

out of the win-dow, stay-ing out of the sun. So I chose free - dom,

Run-ning a round try-ing ev-ry-thing new; but no-thing im-pressed me at all, I

**Slow Tango feel**

nev - er ex-pect-ed it to. Don't cry for me Ar-gen - ti - na,____ the

truth is I nev - er left you: All through my wild days, my mad ex -

-ist-ence, I kept my prom-ise, Don't keep your dis-tance.

3. And as for for-tune and as for fame — I nev-er in-vi-ted them in:

Though it seemed to the world they were all I de-sired. They are il-

-lu - - sions, they're not the so-lu - tions they prom-ised to be, the

an-swer was here all the time I love you and hope you love me.

**Slower**

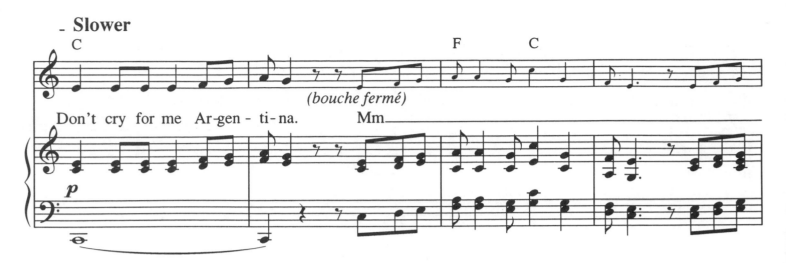

Don't cry for me Ar-gen-ti-na.  Mm____ (bouche fermé)

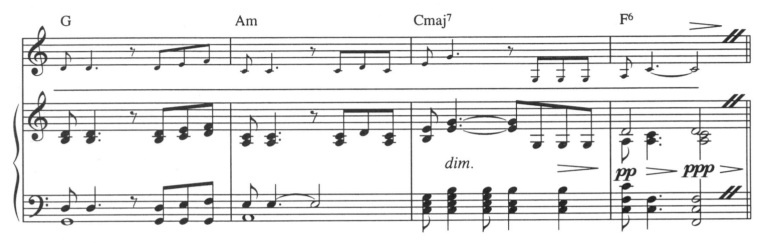

**Tempo I°**

Don't cry for me Ar-gen-ti-na____ the truth is I nev-er left you:  All through my

wild days  my mad ex-ist-ence,  I kept my prom-ise,  Don't keep your dis-tance.__

Have I said too much? There's no-thing more I can think of to say to you

But all you have to do is

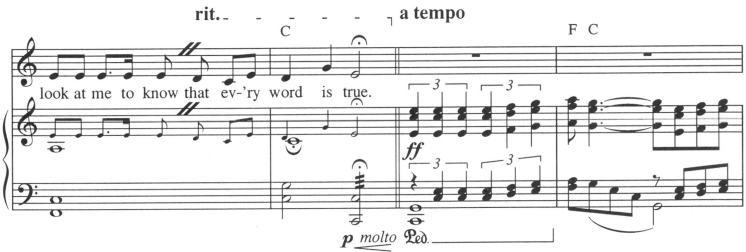

look at me to know that ev-'ry word is true.

# Diamonds Are A Girl's Best Friend

Words by Leo Robin
Music by Jule Styne

**Bright swing**

A

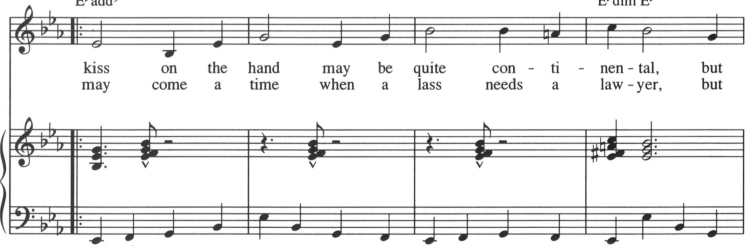

kiss on the hand may be quite con-ti-nen-tal, but
may come a time when a lass needs a law-yer, but

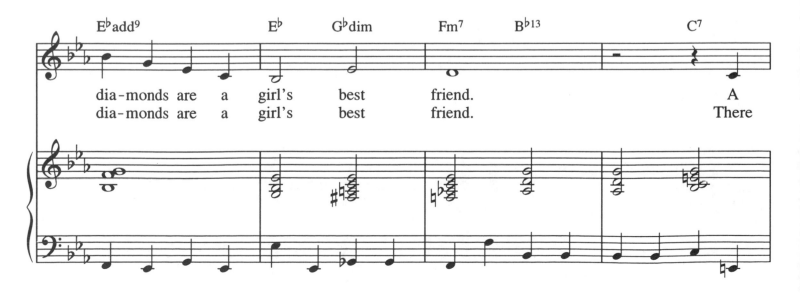

dia-monds are a girl's best friend.
dia-monds are a girl's best friend.

A
There

kiss may be grand but it won't pay the ren - tal on your
may come a time when a hard - boiled em - ploy - er thinks you're

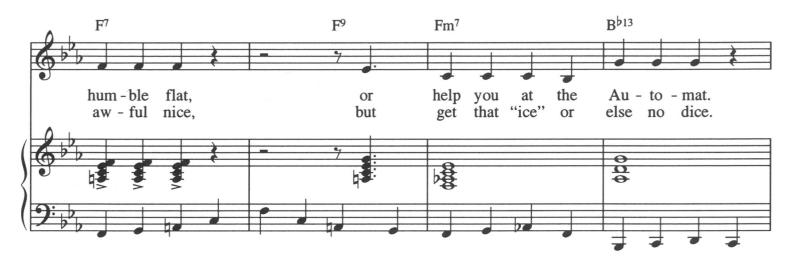

hum - ble flat, or help you at the Au - to - mat.
aw - ful nice, but get that "ice" or else no dice.

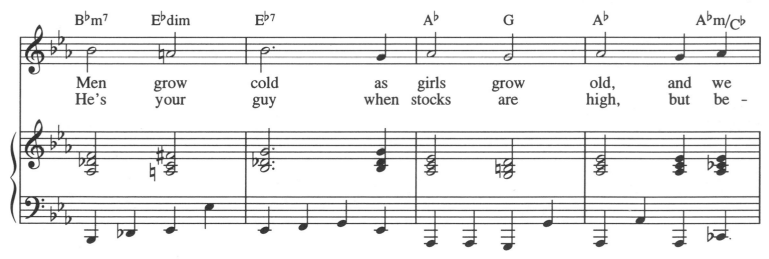

Men grow cold as girls grow old, and we
He's your guy when stocks grow are high, but be -

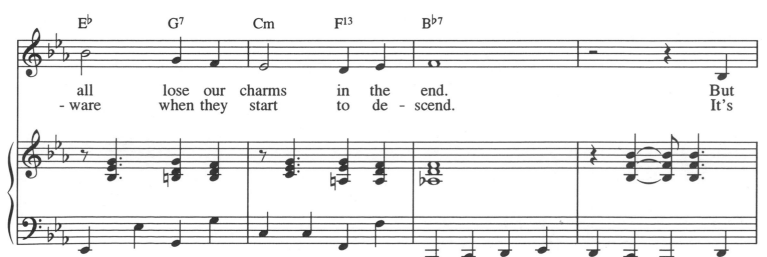

all lose our charms in the end. But
- ware when they start to de - scend. It's

square - cut or pear - shape these rocks don't lose their shape.
then that those lous - es go back to their spous - es,

Dia - monds are a girl's best friend.
dia - monds are a girl's best

There friend.

Dia - monds are a girl's best friend.

# Feeling Good

### Words & Music by Leslie Bricusse & Anthony Newley

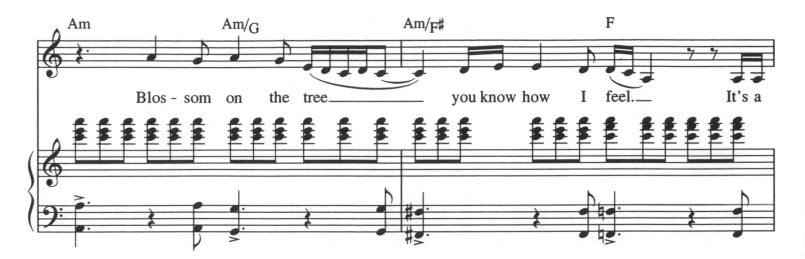

Blos - som on the tree _____ you know how I feel. ___ It's a

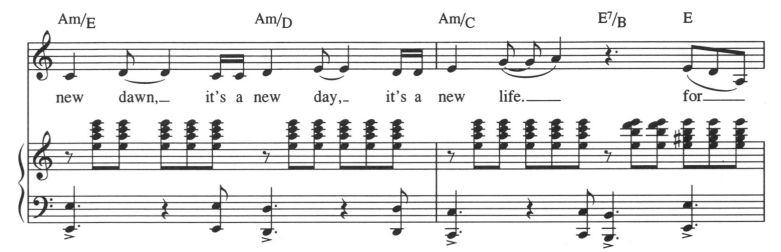

new dawn, ___ it's a new day, __ it's a new life. ___ for ___

me. _____ And I'm feel - ing good.

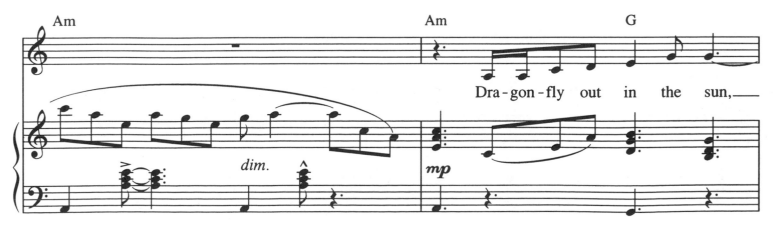

Dra - gon - fly out in the sun, ___

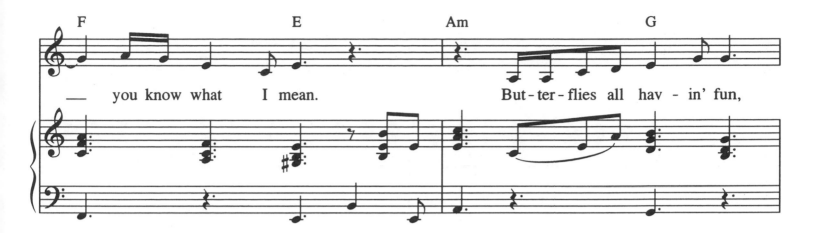

_you know what I mean._

Butterflies all havin' fun,

you know what I mean.

Sleep in peace when day is done,

that's what I mean.

And this old world is a new world, and a

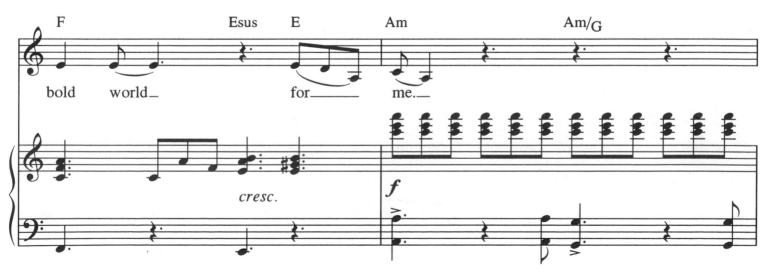

bold world for me.

cresc.

_f_

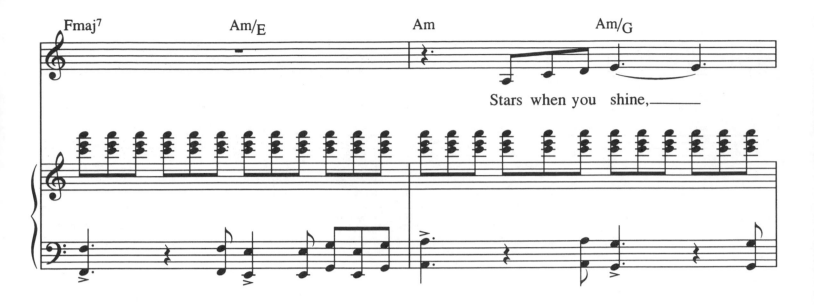

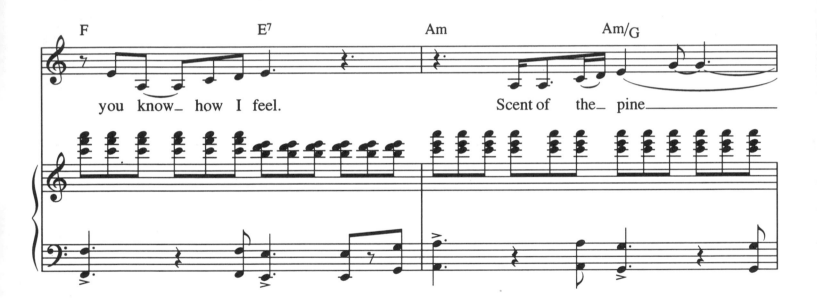

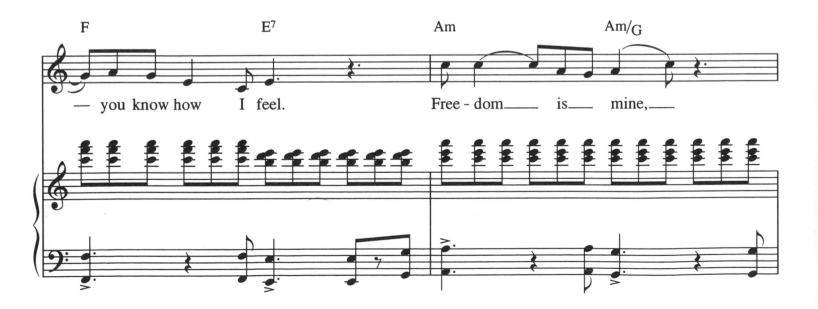

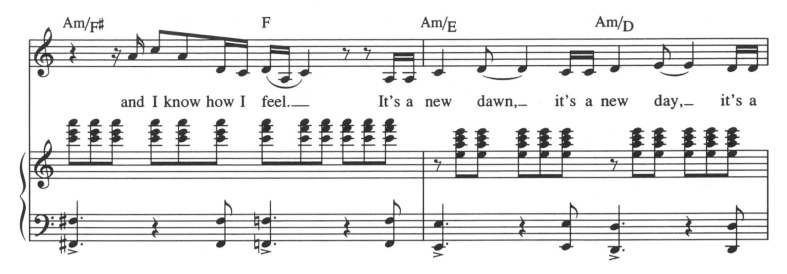

and I know how I feel.___ It's a new dawn,___ it's a new day,___ it's a

**poco rall.**

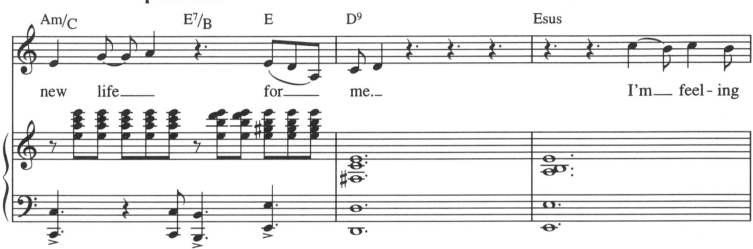

new life___ for___ me.___ I'm___ feel-ing

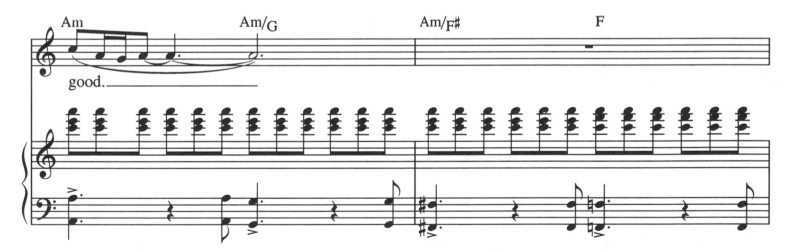

good._____

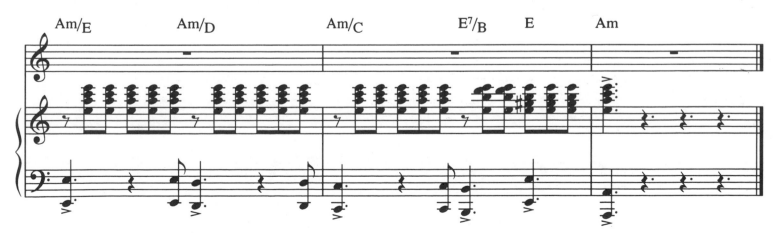

# Heaven Help My Heart

## Words & Music by Benny Andersson, Tim Rice & Bjorn Ulvaeus

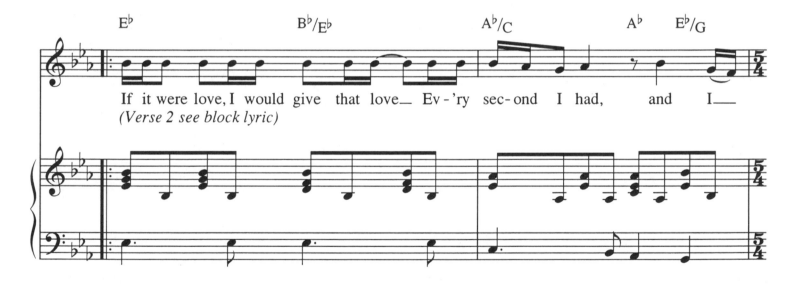

If it were love, I would give that love— Ev-'ry sec-ond I had, and I—
*(Verse 2 see block lyric)*

do._____ Did I know where he'd lead me to? Did— I_____

plan Do-ing all of this for the love of a man?— Well, I let it

hap-pen an-y-how;— And what I'm feel-ing now Has no eas-y ex-pla-na-tion,

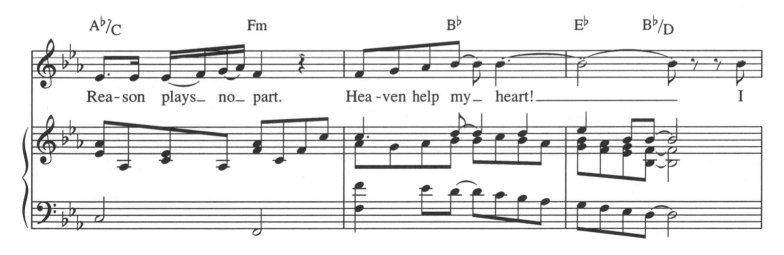

Rea-son plays— no— part. Hea-ven help my— heart!_____ I

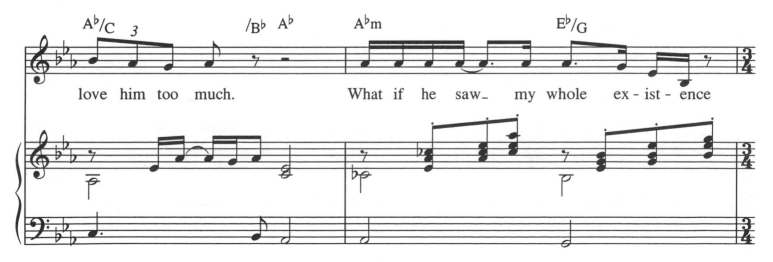

love him too much. What if he saw— my whole ex-ist-ence

Turn-ing a-round_ a word, a smile, a touch?_____

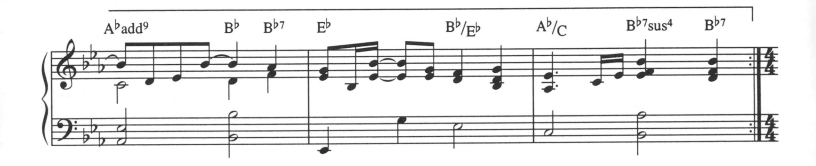

mind.                    May-be it's best_ to love_ a stran-ger;____ But

that's what I've done, Hea-ven help    my___ heart!

**Molto rit.**

Hea - ven_ help_ my_ heart.

*Verse 2*

One of these days, and it won't be long,
He'll know more about me than he should.
All my dreams will be understood:
No surprise.
Nothing more to learn from the look in my eyes.
Don't you know that time is not my friend?
I'll fight it to the end,
Hoping to keep the best of moments
When the passions start.
Heaven help my heart
The day that I find
Suddenly I've run out of secrets,
Suddenly I'm not always on his mind!

# I Cain't Say No

## Words by Oscar Hammerstein II
## Music by Richard Rodgers

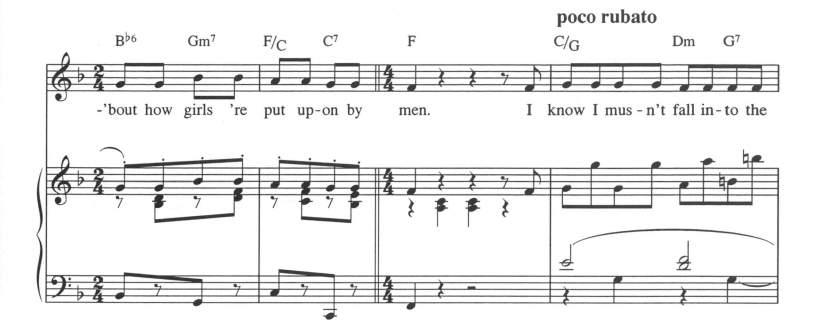

-'bout how girls 're put up-on by men. I know I mus-n't fall in-to the

pit,_____ But when I'm with a fel-ler I fer - git!

I'm jist a girl who cain't say no,
I'm jist a girl who cain't say no,

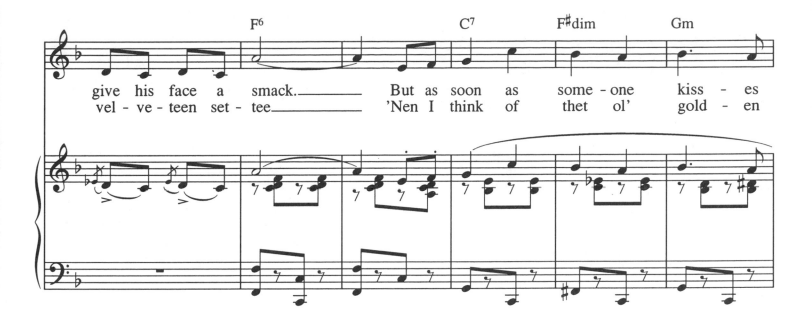

give his face a smack._____ But as soon as some - one kiss - es
vel - ve - teen set - tee_____ 'Nen I think of thet ol' gold - en

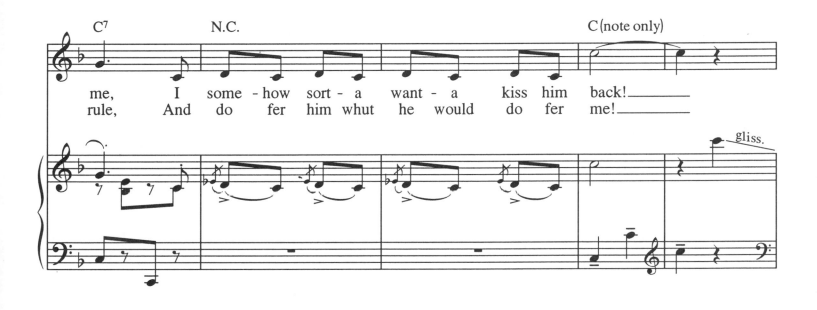

me, I some - how sort - a want - a kiss him back!_____
rule, And do fer him whut he would do fer me!_____

I'm jist a fool when lights are low, I cain't be pris - sy and
I cain't re - sist a Ro - me - o, In a som - bre - ro and

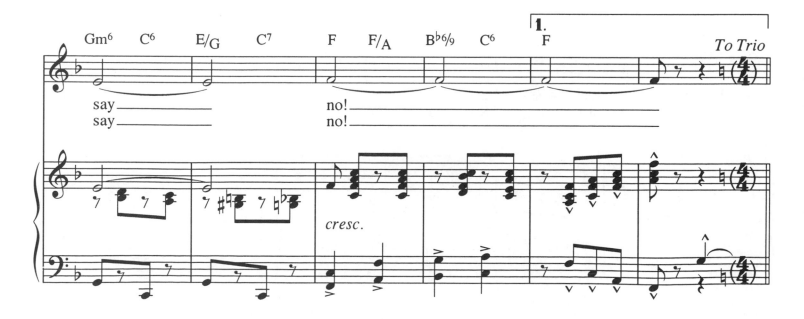

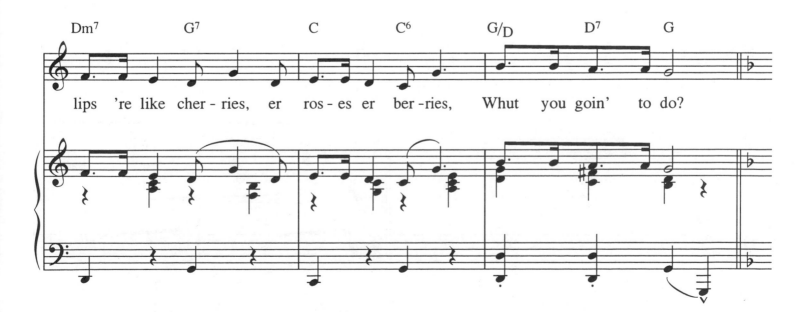

55

S'pos-in' 'at he says 'at yer sweet-er 'n cream and he's got-ta have cream or

die? Whut you goin' to do when he talks thet way?

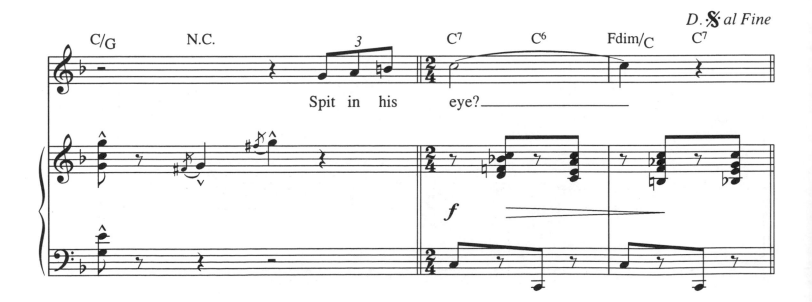

Spit in his eye?

# I Don't Know How To Love Him

Music by Andrew Lloyd Webber
Lyrics by Tim Rice

**Slowly**

I don't know how to

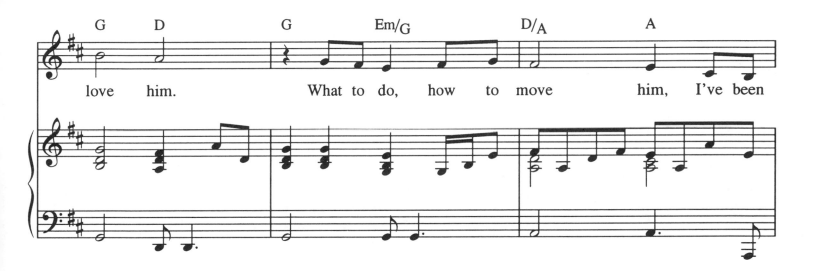

love him. What to do, how to move him, I've been

changed yes real-ly changed In these past few days— when I've

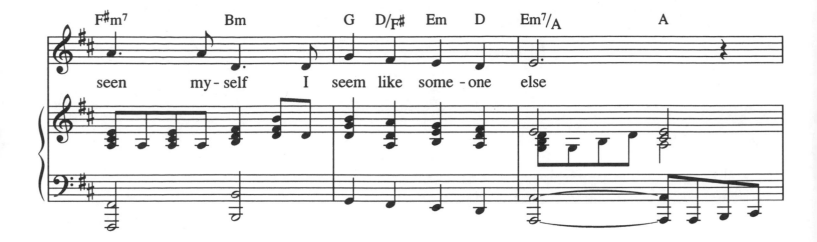

seen my-self I seem like some-one else

I don't know how to take this I don't see why he

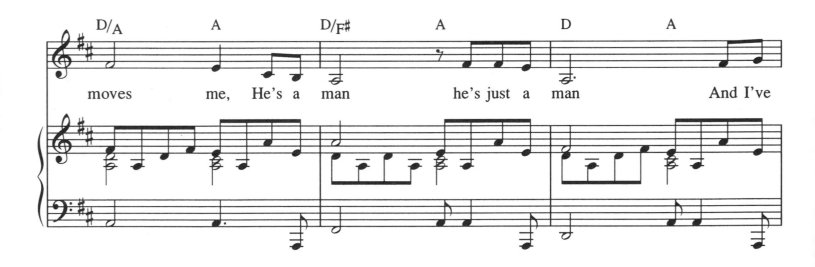

moves me, He's a man he's just a man And I've

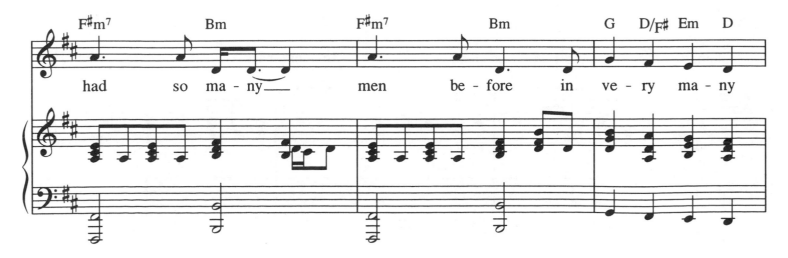

had so ma-ny___ men be-fore in ve-ry ma-ny

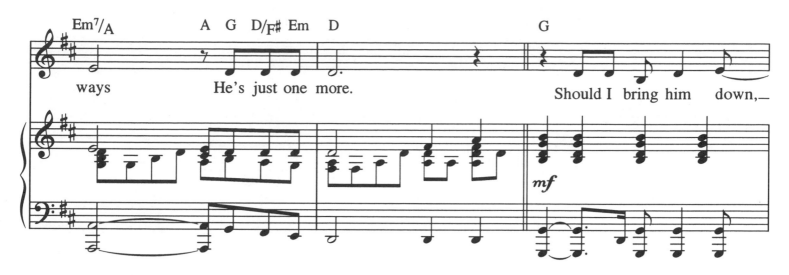

ways He's just one more. Should I bring him down,—

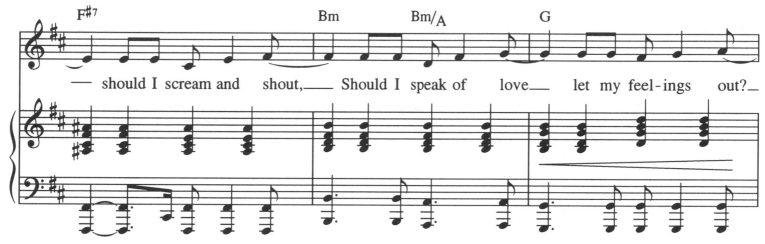

— should I scream and shout,— Should I speak of love— let my feel-ings out?—

— I ne-ver thought I'd come to this— what's it all a-

- bout?
Don't you think it's ra-ther
Yet if he said he

*To Coda* ⊕

60

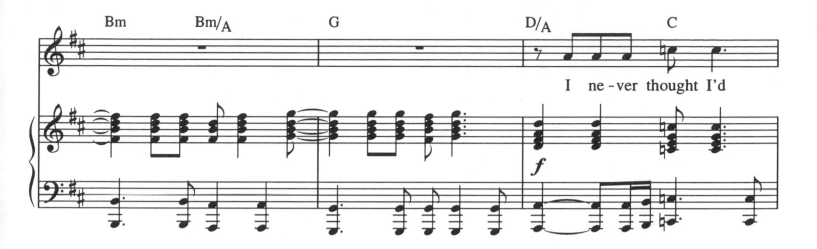

I ne-ver thought I'd

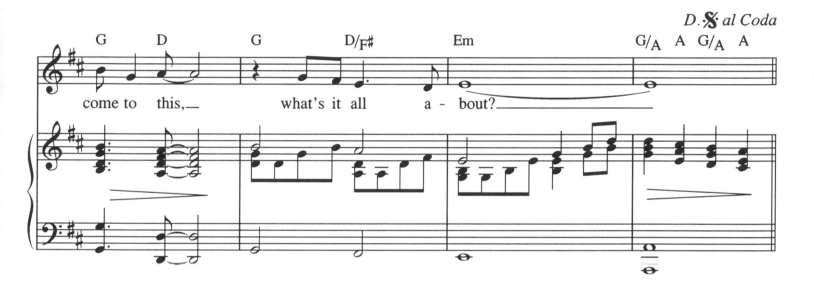

come to this,— what's it all a - bout?—

*D. %. al Coda*

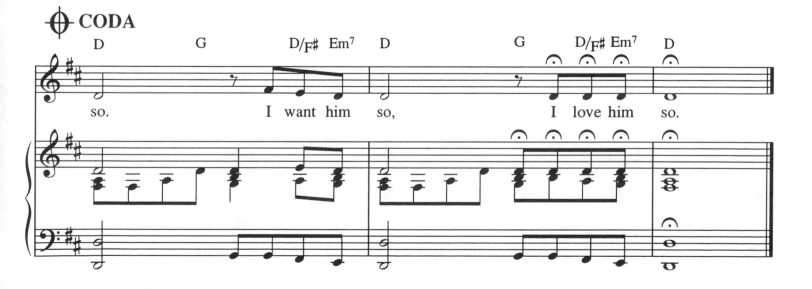

CODA

so. I want him so, I love him so.

# I Dreamed A Dream
## (From The Musical 'Les Misérables')

Music by Claude-Michel Schönberg. Lyric by Herbert Kretzmer
Original Text by Alain Boublil & Jean-Marc Natel

And there are storms we can-not wea - ther.___

I had a dream my life would be    So diffe-rent from this hell I'm

li - ving;___ so diffe-rent now from what it seemed,    Now life has killed the dream I

dreamed.

# I Say A Little Prayer

Words by Hal David
Music by Burt Bacharach

**Bright rock**

1. The mo-ment I
(Verse 2 see block lyric)

wake up, be-fore I put on my make-up, I

say a lit-tle prayer for you.___ While comb-ing my

hair now, and won-d'ring what dress___ to___ wear now, I

say a lit-tle prayer for you.___ For-ev-er for-ev-er you'll

stay in my heart___ and I will love you for-ev-er and ev-er we

nev - er will part,__ oh how I'll love you, to - geth - er, to-geth - er, that's

how it must be.__ To live with - out you would on - ly mean heart-break for

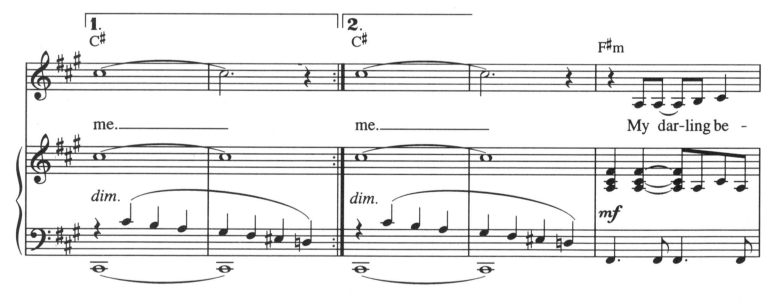

me._____  me._____  My dar-ling be -

- lieve me, for me__ there is no - one_____ but

68

you.   Please— love me too._____  I'm— in love with

you._____  An-swer my prayer._____  Say you love me

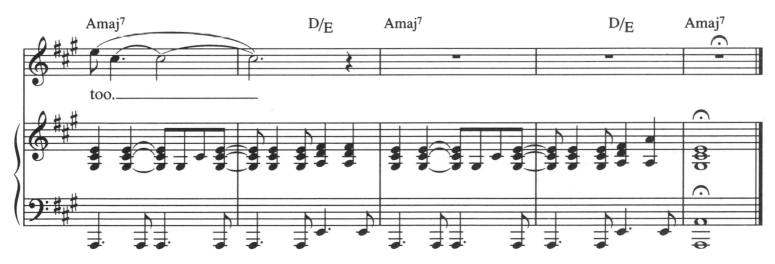

too._____

*Verse 2:*
I run for the bus, dear;
While riding, I think of us dear.
I say a little prayer for you.
At work I just take time,
And all through my coffee break time
I say a little prayer for you.

Forever, forever, *etc.*

# I Will Survive

## Words & Music by Dino Fekaris & Freddie Perren

At first I was a-fraid, I was pet-ri-fied,___ kept think-in'

I could nev-er live___with-out you by my side; but then I spent so ma-ny nights___ think-in'

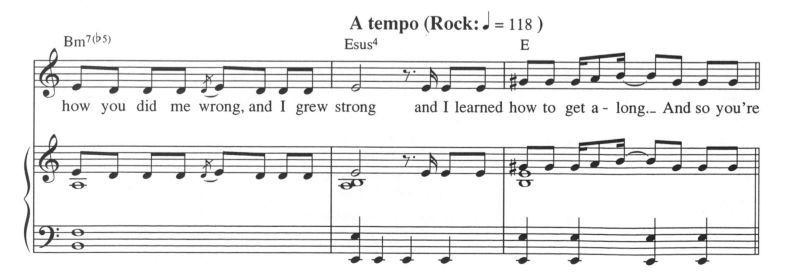

how you did me wrong, and I grew strong and I learned how to get a - long.___ And so you're

back from out-er space  I just walked in to find you here with that sad
me, some bod-y new,  I'm not that chained up lit-tle per - son still in love 

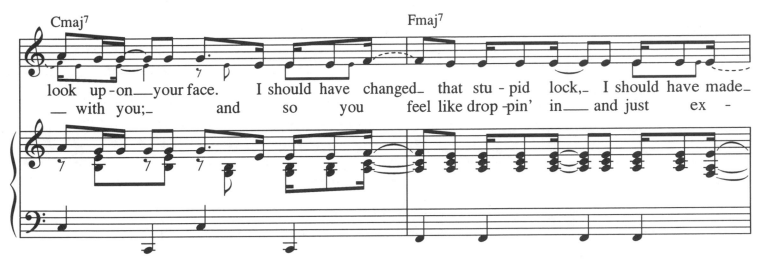

look up-on your face. I should have changed that stu - pid lock, I should have made 
 with you; and so you feel like drop-pin' in and just ex -

 you leave your key if I'd-'ve known for just one sec - ond you'd be
-pect me to be free, now I'm sav - in' all my lov - in' for some

back to both - er me. Go on now } Go walk out the door just turn a-round 
one who's lov-in' me. Go on now }

now 'cause you're not wel-come an-y-more.___ Weren't you the one___ who tried to hurt___

___ me with good-bye?___ Did I crum-ble,___ did you think I'd lay down___ and die? Oh no, not

I. I will sur-vive,___ oh___ as long as I know how to love___ I

know I'll stay a-live. I've got all my life to live, I've got all my love to give___ and I'll sur-vive.___

I will sur-vive._____ Hey, hey!\_\_\_

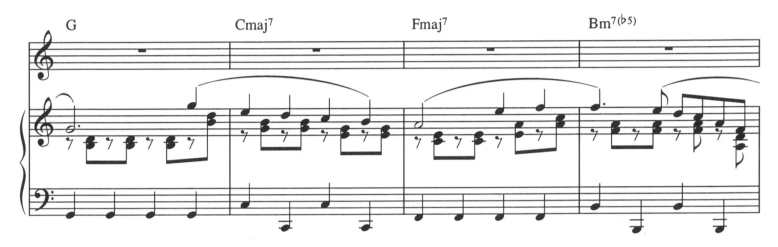

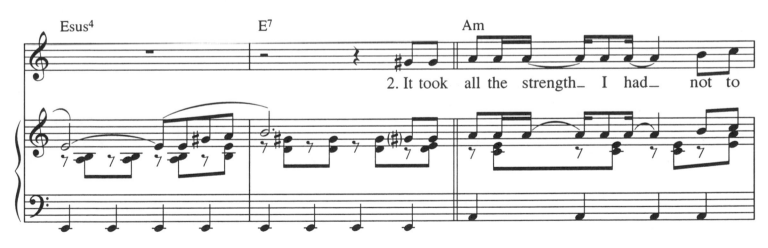

2. It took all the strength\_ I had\_ not to

fall a-part,_____ kept try-in' hard to mend\_ the piec-es of my bro-

-ken heart;___ and I spent oh so man-y nights___ just feel-in'

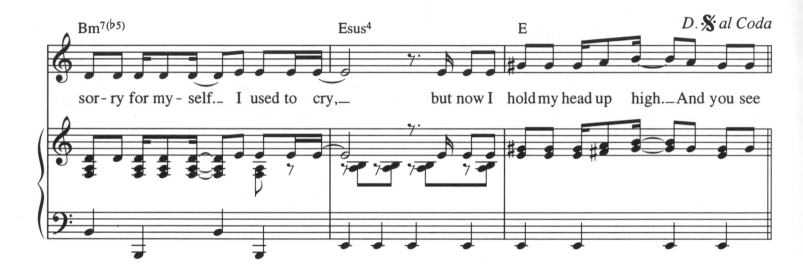

sor-ry for my-self.___ I used to cry,___ but now I hold my head up high.___And you see

I'll sur - vive.___

# If I Were A Bell

## Words & Music by Frank Loesser

**Gentle swing** (♩ = 116)

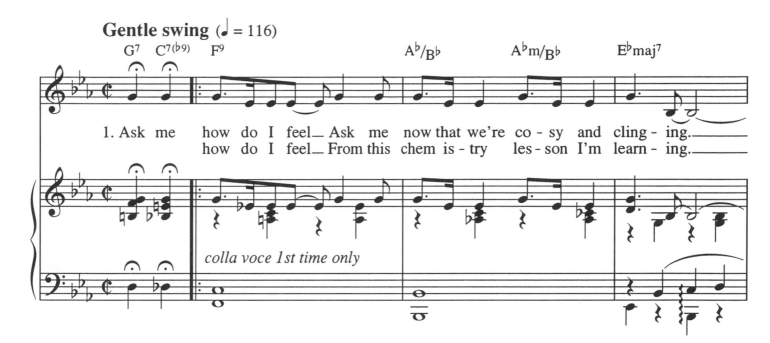

1. Ask me how do I feel___ Ask me now that we're co-sy and cling-ing.___
   how do I feel___ From this chem-is-try les-son I'm learn-ing.___

*colla voce 1st time only*

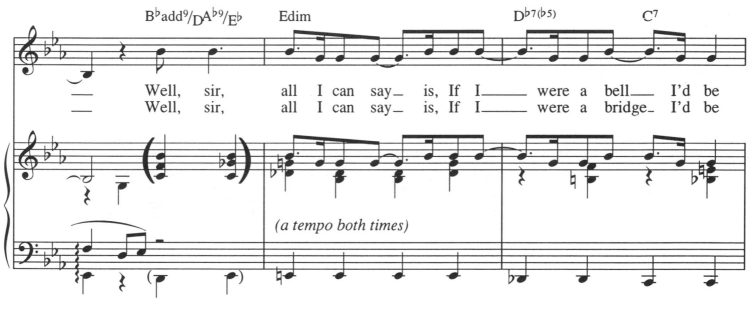

___ Well, sir, all I can say___ is, If I___ were a bell___ I'd be
___ Well, sir, all I can say___ is, If I___ were a bridge___ I'd be

*(a tempo both times)*

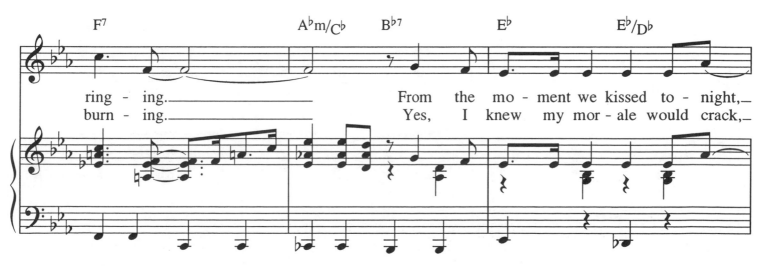

ring-ing.___ From the mo-ment we kissed to-night,
burn-ing.___ Yes, I knew my mor-ale would crack,___

75

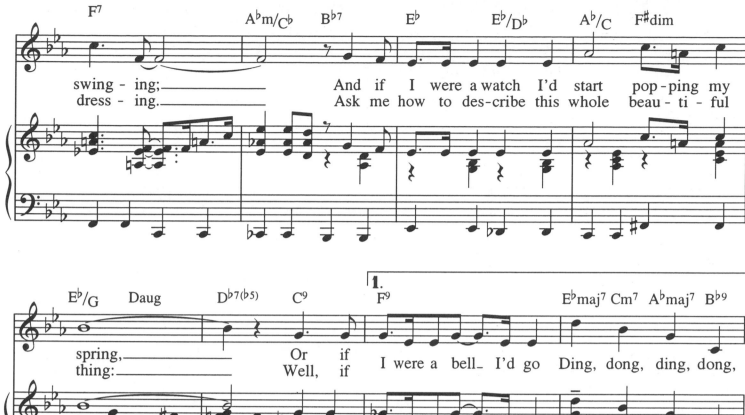

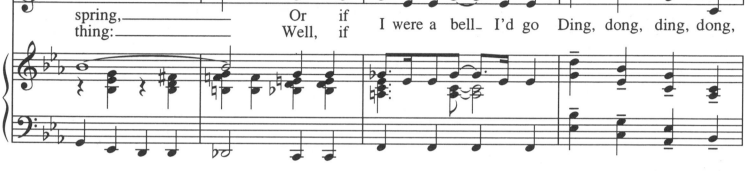

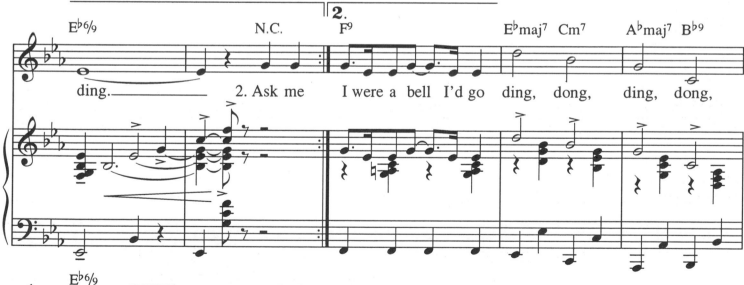

# If My Friends Could See Me Now

Words by Dorothy Fields
Music by Cy Coleman

**Bright 2**

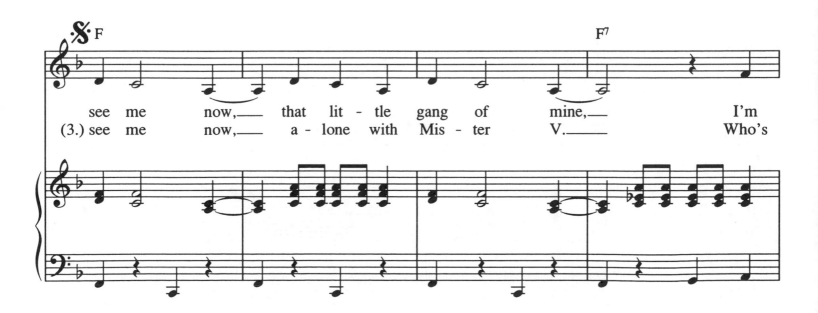

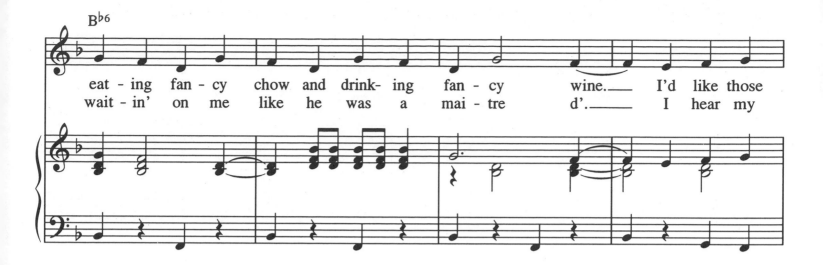

eat - ing fan - cy chow and drink- ing fan - cy wine.___ I'd like those
wait - in' on me like he was a mai - tre d'.___ I hear my

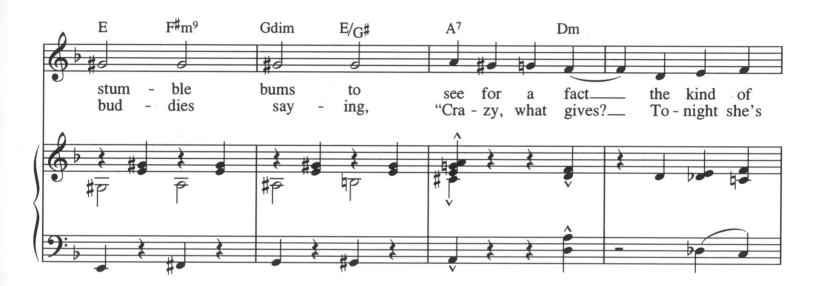

stum - ble bums to see for a fact___ the kind of
bud - dies say - ing, "Cra - zy, what gives?___ To - night she's

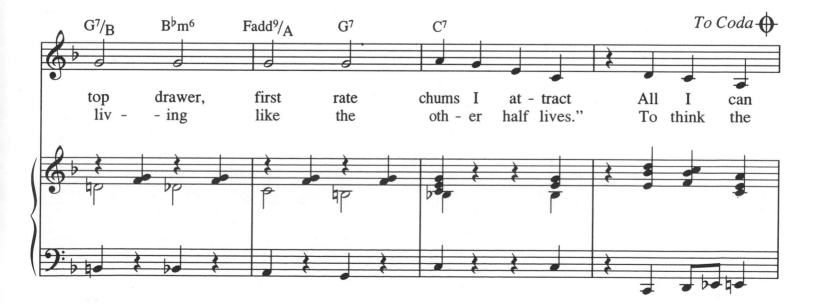

*To Coda*

top drawer, first rate chums I at - tract All I can
liv - ing like the oth - er half lives." To think the

79

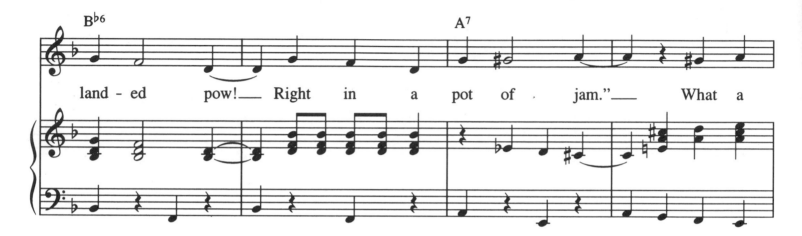

2. If they could

see me now,___ my lit - tle dust - y group,___

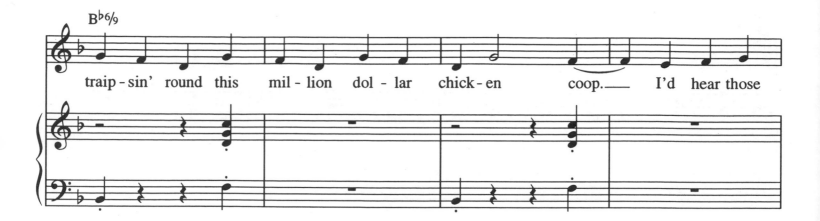

traip - sin' round this mil - lion dol - lar chick - en coop.___ I'd hear those

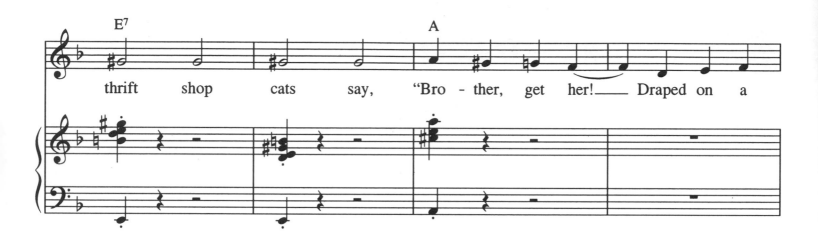

thrift shop cats say, "Bro - ther, get her!___ Draped on a

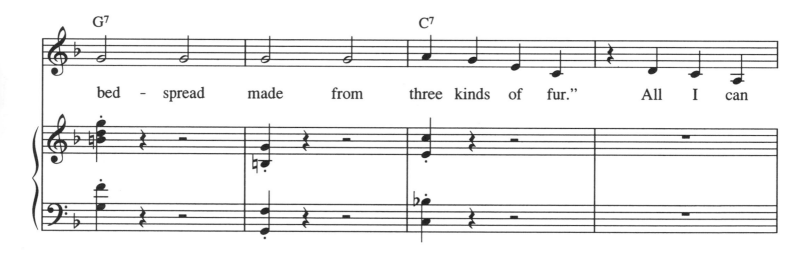

bed - spread made from three kinds of fur." All I can

say is Wow!___ Wait till the riff and raff___ see just ex -

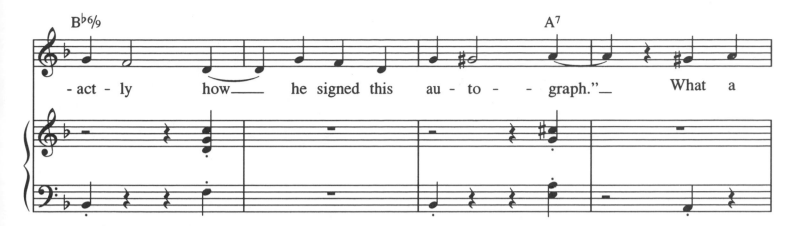

-act - ly how____ he signed this au - to - - graph."____ What a

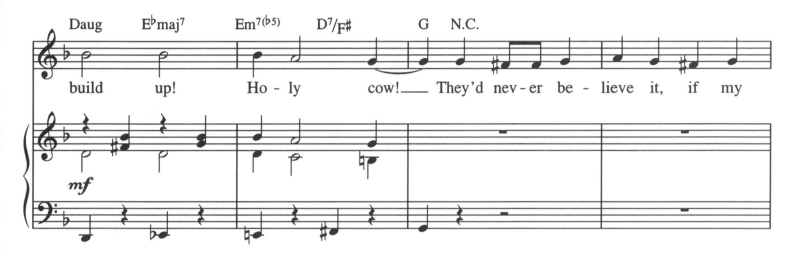

build up! Ho - ly cow!____ They'd nev - er be - lieve it, if my

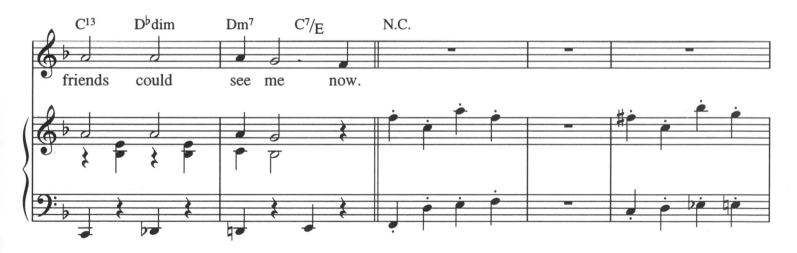

friends could see me now.

*D. %. al Coda*

3. If they could

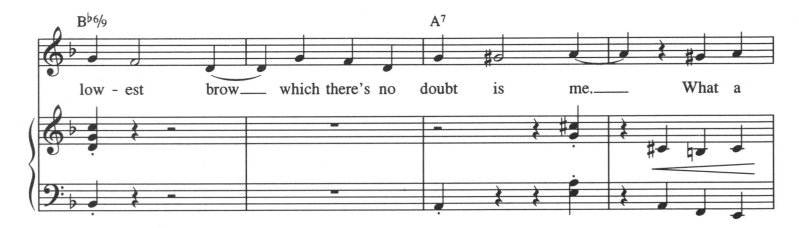

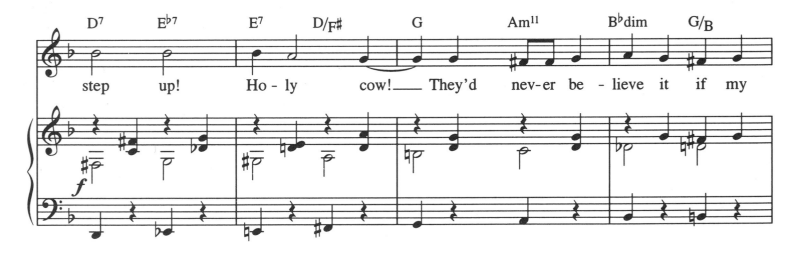

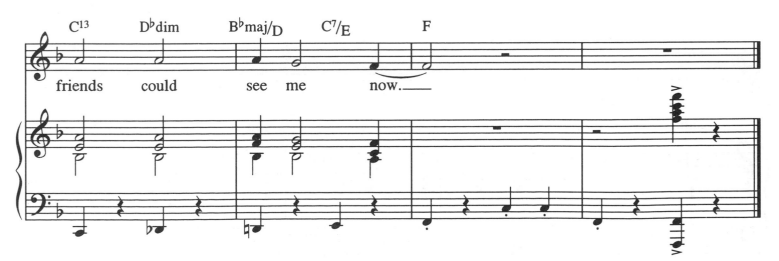

# It's Oh So Quiet

### Words & Music by Hans Lang, Bert Reisfeld & Erich Meder

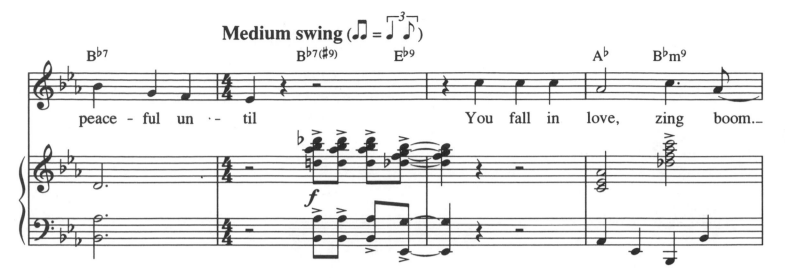

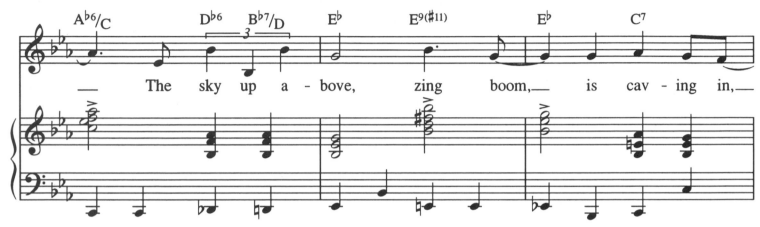

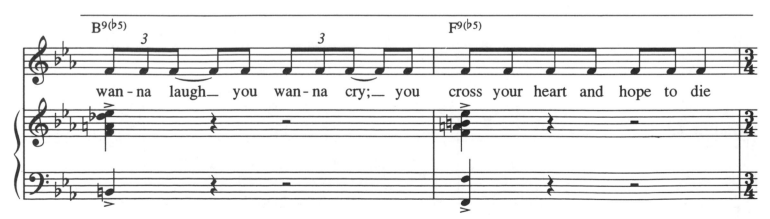

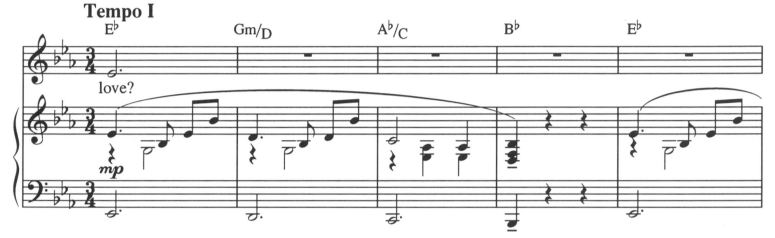

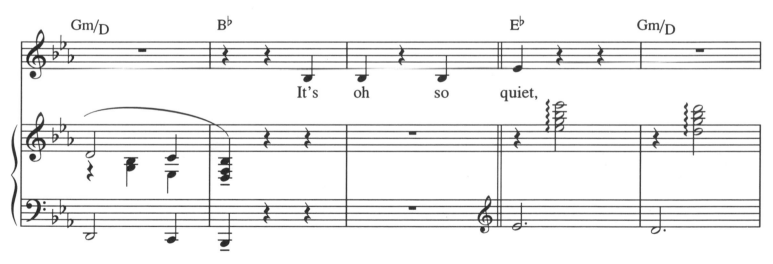

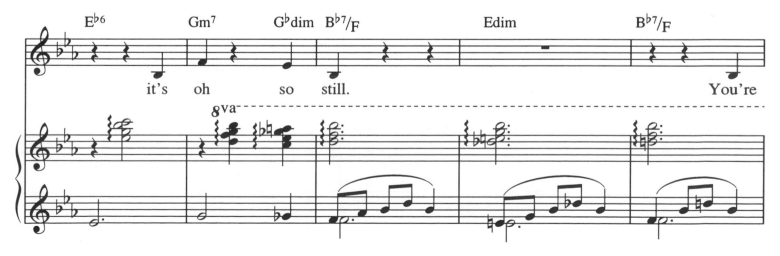

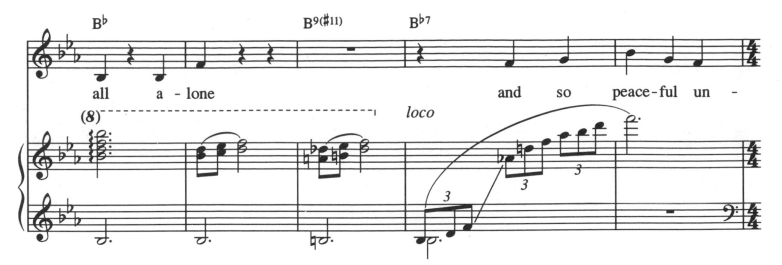

all a - lone and so peace-ful un -

**Tempo 2**

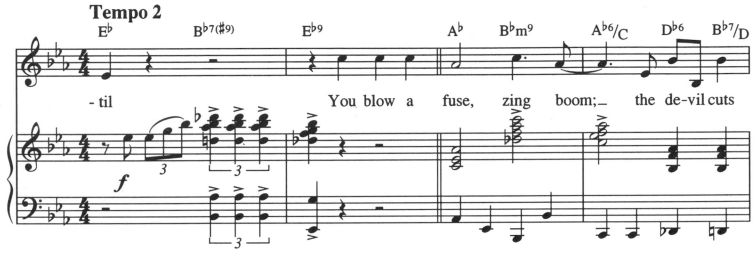

-til You blow a fuse, zing boom;— the de-vil cuts

loose, zing boom.— So what's the use,— wow bam,— of fall - ing in love?—

The sky caves in, the

*Verse 2:*
And then it's nice and quiet.
But soon again starts another big riot.
You blow a fuse, zing boom,
The devil cuts loose, zing boom.
So what's the use, wow bam,
Of falling in love?

# Memory

### Music by Andrew Lloyd Webber
### Text by Trevor Nunn after T.S. Eliot

me - - mory_____ live_____ a - gain.

**poco più mosso**

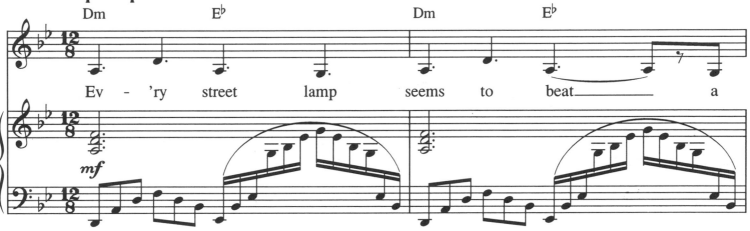

Ev - 'ry street lamp seems to beat_____ a

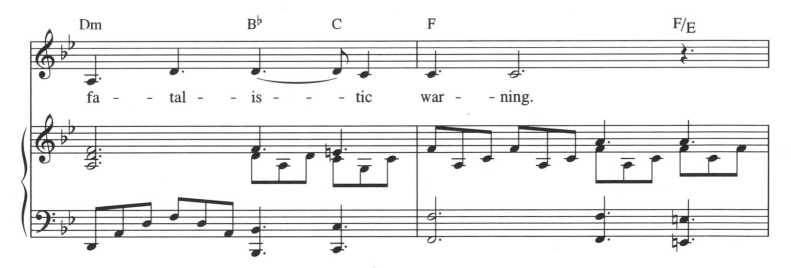

fa - tal - is - - - tic war - - ning.

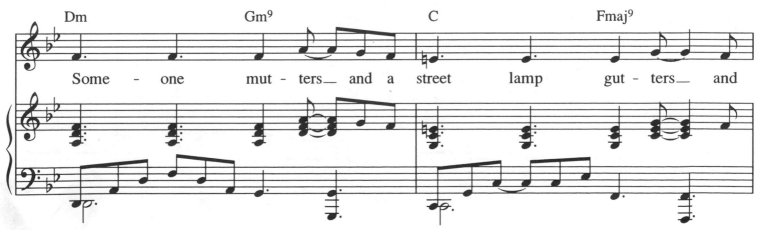

Some - one mut - ters_____ and a street lamp gut - ters_____ and

new day_____ will_ be - gin.

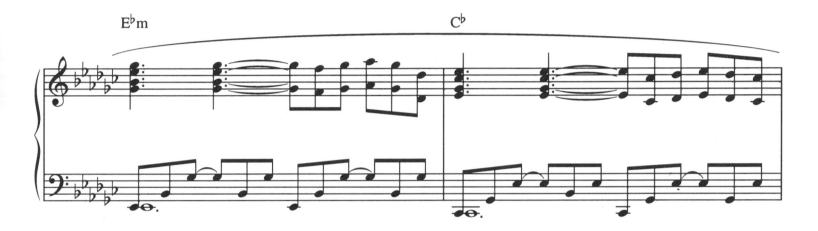

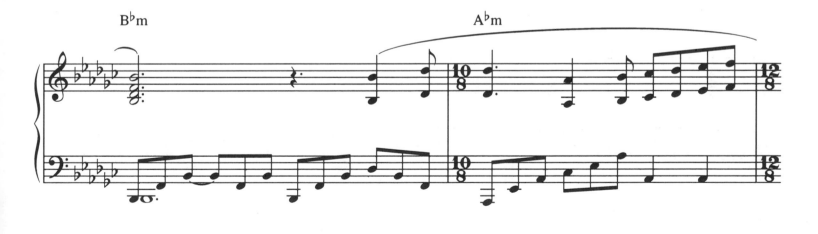

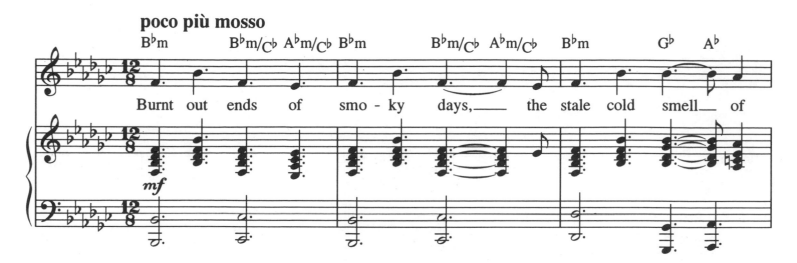

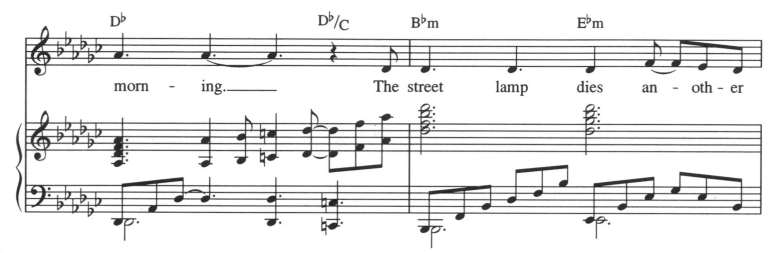

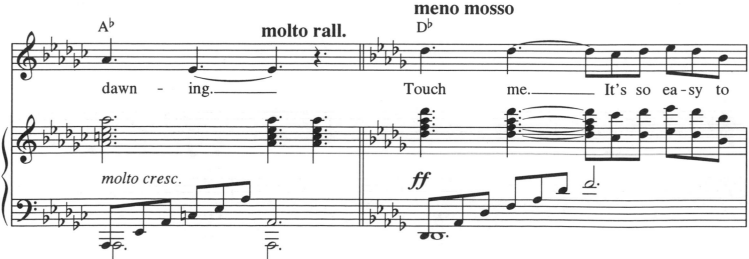

94

leave me _____ All a-lone with the me - m'ry _____ Of my days in the

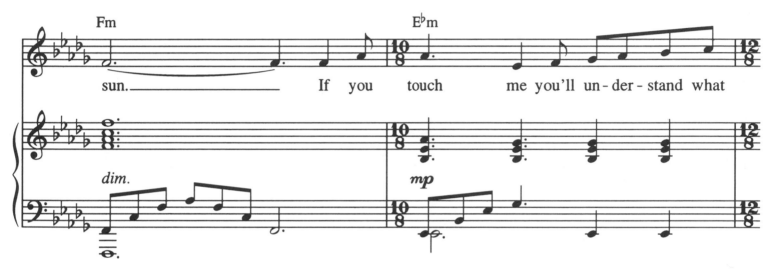

sun. _____ If you touch me you'll un-der-stand what

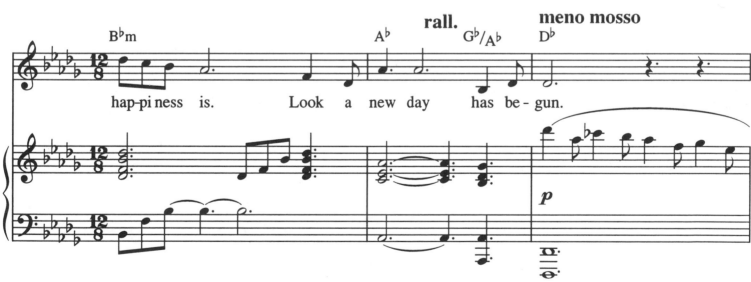

hap-pi ness is. Look a new day has be - gun.

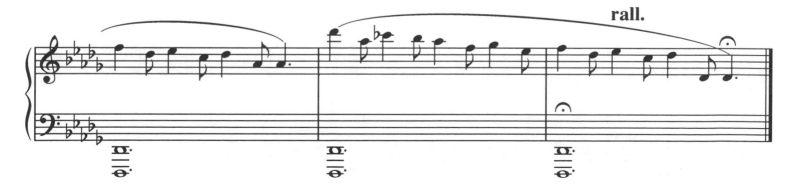

# Miss Byrd

## Music by David Shire
## Words by Richard Maltby Jr.

1. The sign says I'm Miss Byrd,— And that's my name.— I'm one of those peo-
*(Verse 2 see block lyric)*

- ple who all— look the same.— At work I'm hard - ly seen.— I come and go,

Fm¹¹     Dm⁷⁽♭⁵⁾     G⁷⁽♭⁹⁾

— But I know some-thing that peo - ple don't know.—

Cmaj⁹     G⁷⁽♭⁹⁾aug     Cmaj⁹

Ev - 'ry-one who sees— me thinks— That I'm that dull Miss Byrd.
*(Verse 3 see block lyric)*

F   F⁷aug     B♭maj⁹     F⁷⁽♭⁹⁾aug

— I could blow that myth— a - part,— But

97

her heart takes wing,— This bird is sing - - - ing.—

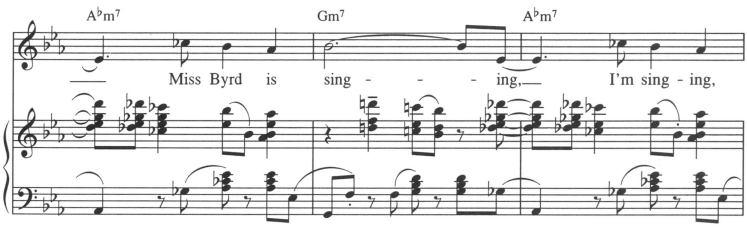

Miss Byrd is sing - - ing,— I'm sing - ing,

*To* ⊕ *Coda*

1.

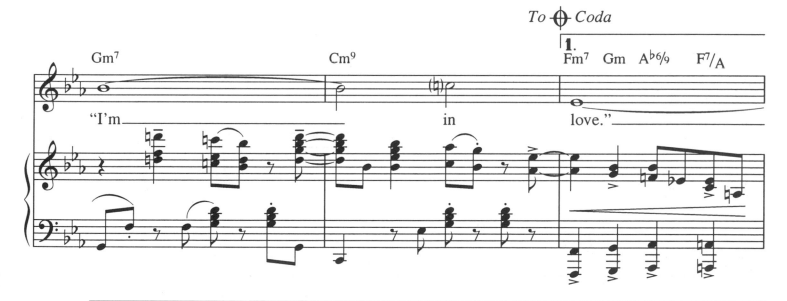

"I'm ____ in love." ____

— But I'm not say - ing a thing.— *Uh - huh*

100

## ⊕ CODA

*Verse 2*
Down in Apartment 'A', the Super's aptly named.
Last week I went to the basement more hours than I claimed.
He says I'm super, too; he calls me hot.
I show those basement apartments a lot!
Back at work I'm crisp and fresh, reliable Miss Byrd.
Seals are dancing in my flesh, but I don't say a word.
I'm showing Penthouse 'C'; as I begin,
I still feel his hands sliding over my skin.
My nipples start to throb inside my bra;
That's when I start to go "Lah dah di dah".
If you've never felt the lift a little lunch can bring,
This bird is singing; Miss Byrd is singing.
I'm singing "I'm on fire!", but I'm not saying a thing.

*Verse 3*
Lots of girls who first seem shy have secrets, I have found.
If you think I'm special, I suggest you look around.
That little office temp who seems so dumb,
How come a trip to MacDonald's is making her hum?
And Mrs Smith in Sales, who's turning grey,
Why is she smiling that curious way?
If it's true the drabbest song-birds come alive in Spring,
The birds are singing; Miss Byrd is singing.
I'm singing "I'm in love!", but I'm not saying a thing.

# Killing Me Softly With His Song

Words by Norman Gimbel
Music by Charles Fox

**Moderately**

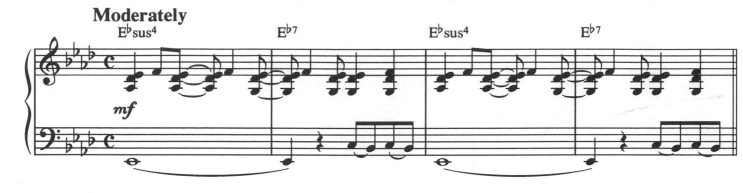

1. I heard he sang a good song, I heard he had a style.
*(Verses 2 & 3 see block lyric)*

And so I came to see him and lis-ten for a while.

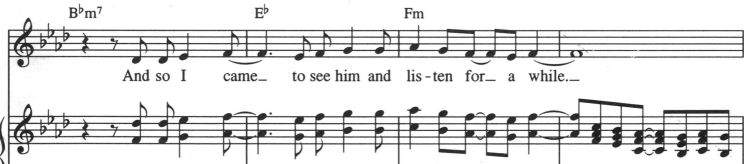

And there he was this young boy, a stran-ger to my eyes.

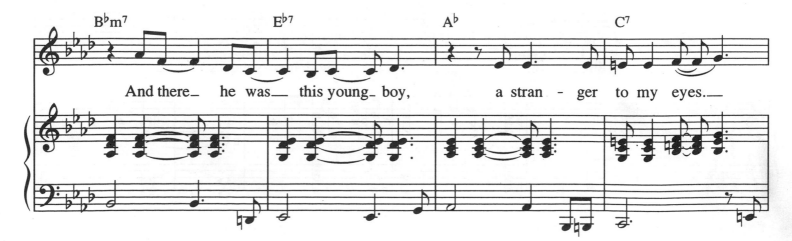

Strum-ming my pain__ with his fin - gers,__ sing-ing my life__with his words..

__ Kill -ing me soft - ly with his__ song, kill -ing me soft -

- ly_____ with his__ song, tell -ing my whole_ life_____ with his__

__words, kill-ing me soft - ly_____ with his song._____

*Verse 2:*
I felt all flushed with fever,
Embarrassed by the crowd.
I felt he found my letters
And read each one out loud.
I prayed that he would finish,
But he just kept right on.

Strumming my pain *etc.*

*Verse 3:*
He sang as if he knew me
In all my dark despair.
And then he looked right through me
As if I wasn't there.
But he was there this stranger,
Singing clear and strong.

Strumming my pain *etc.*

# Now That I've Seen Her (Her Or Me)

Music by Claude-Michel Schönberg
Lyrics by Richard Maltby Jr. & Alain Boublil

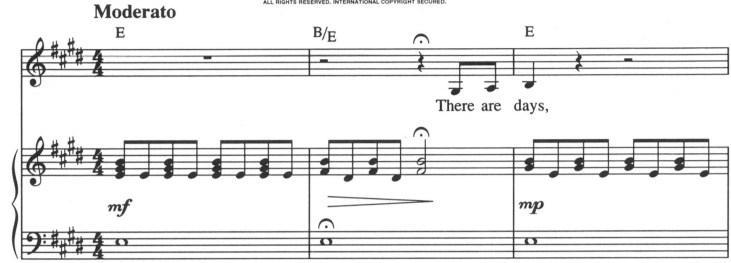

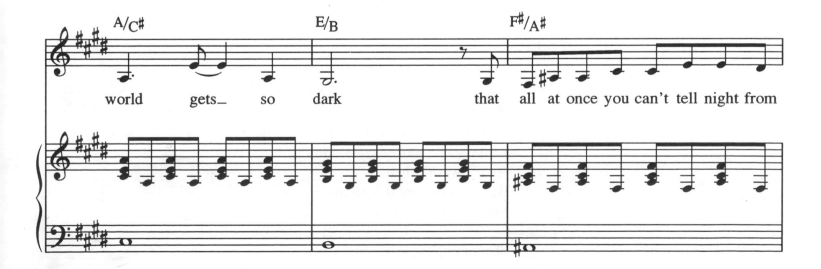

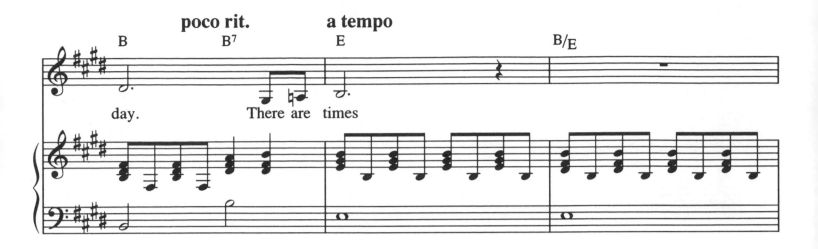

hide,     she is  not some fling__  from  long  a-go.__   Now    that__   I've

seen    her__   I    know    why__   he    lied,          and   I   think    it was

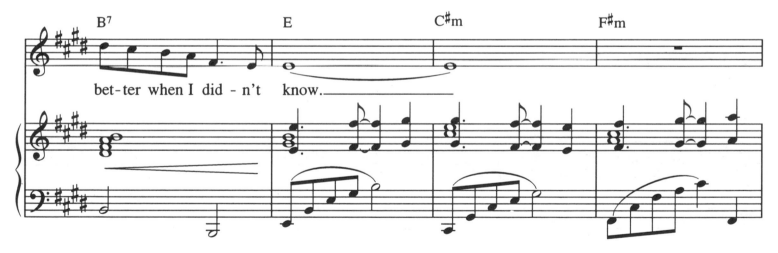

bet-ter when I did - n't   know._____

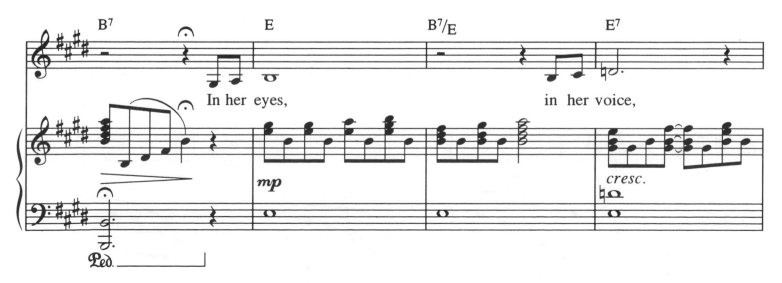

In her eyes,                 in  her voice,

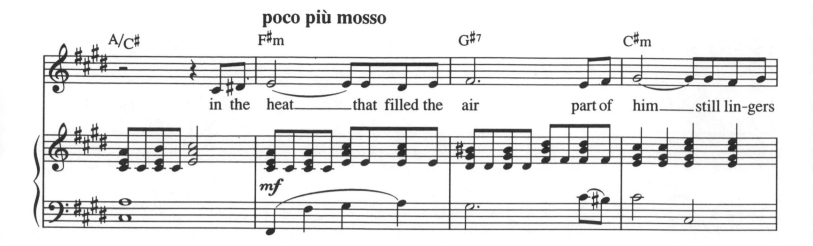

in the heat____ that filled the air part of him____ still lin-gers

there. I know what pain her life to-day must be.

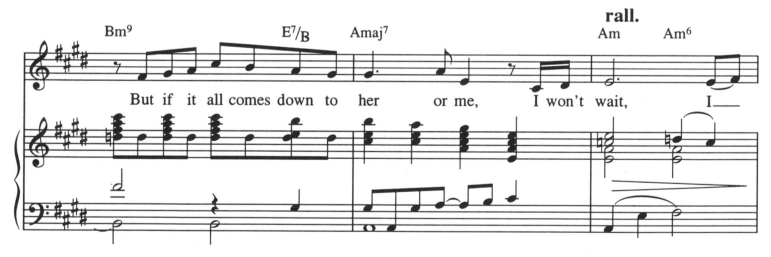

But if it all comes down to her or me, I won't wait, I____

swear____ I'll fight.

Now that— I've seen her— she's more than— a name she is

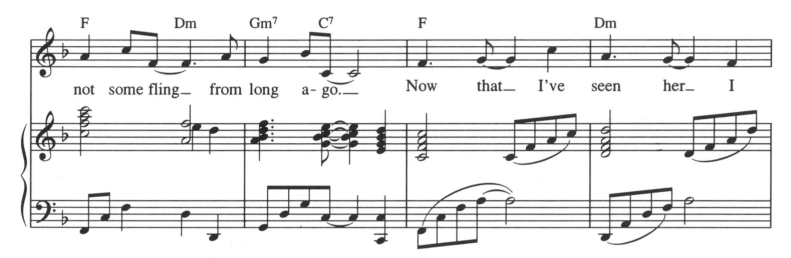

not some fling— from long a-go.— Now that— I've seen her— I

**rall.**

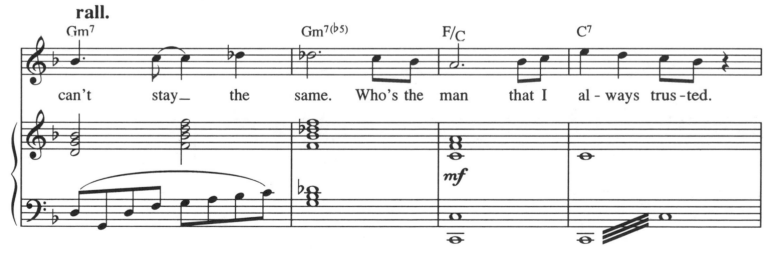

can't stay— the same. Who's the man that I al-ways trus-ted.

**a tempo**  **rall.**

Now I have to know.—————

# Out Here On My Own

## Words & Music by Michael Gore & Lesley Gore

Help me through.__ Help me need you. me need you.

Some-times I won-der where I've been, who I am, do I fit in.

I may not win, but I can't be thrown, out_____ here_____

_____ on my own,_____ on my own.

# The Reason

## Words & Music by Carole King, Mark Hudson & Greg Wells

**Rather slow**

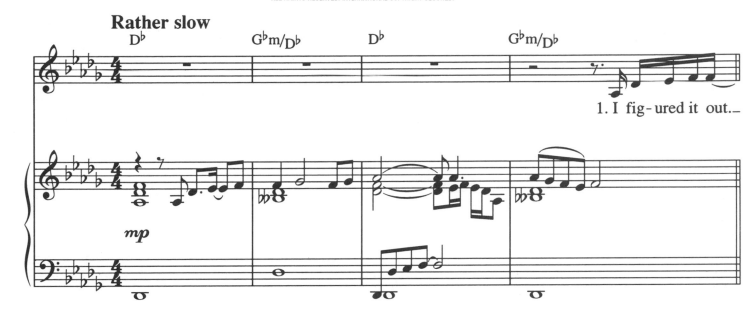

1. I fig-ured it out.__

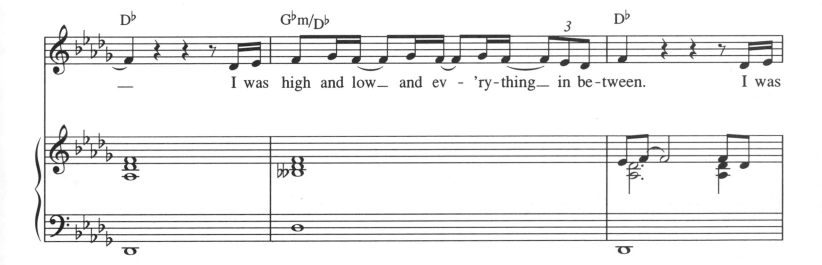

I was high and low__ and ev-'ry-thing__ in be-tween. I was

wick-ed and wild,__ ba-by, you know what I mean, till there was

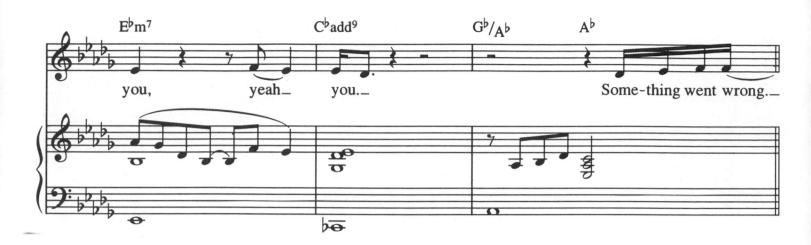

you, yeah_ you._ Some-thing went wrong._

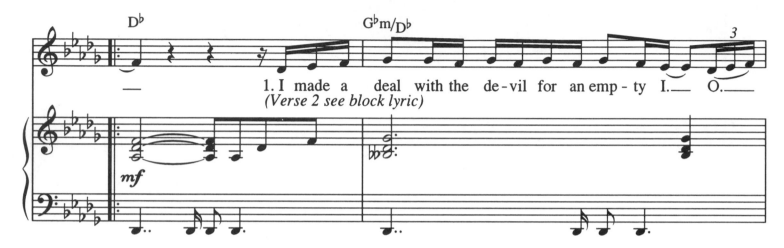

— 1. I made a deal with the de-vil for an emp-ty I._ O._
*(Verse 2 see block lyric)*

U. Been to hell and back_ but an an - gel was look-ing through, it was

you, yeah you,_ it's all be-cause_ of you._ You are the rea-

son.___ you are the rea - son___ I wake up ev-'ry day___ and sleep___

___ through the night,___ you are the rea - son,___ the rea - - son.

In the mid-dle of the night I'm go-ing down___ 'cause {I a-
'cause {I___

dore___ you,} I want___ to floor you.___ I'm giv-ing it up___
want___ you,}

**2.** touch you.__ I want__ to floor you,__ you are__ the rea - son,__ ba - by.

You are the rea - son.__ you are the rea - son__ I wake

up ev-'ry day__ and sleep__ through the night,__ you are the rea - son,__ the

rea - - son, you are the rea- rea- - son.

The rea - - son._____

Be-cause of you___  I was a-lone,

*Verse 2:*
I'm giving it up
No more running around spinning my wheel
You came out of my dream and made it real
I know what I feel, it's you,
It's all because of you.

# Save The Best For Last

## Words & Music by Jon Lind, Wendy Waldman & Philip Galdston

'Cause there was a time  when all  I did  was wish  you'd tell  
'Cause how could you give  your love  to some - one else  and share  

me this  was love.  It's not the way  I hoped or  how  
your dreams  with me?  Some-times the ve - ry thing you're look-

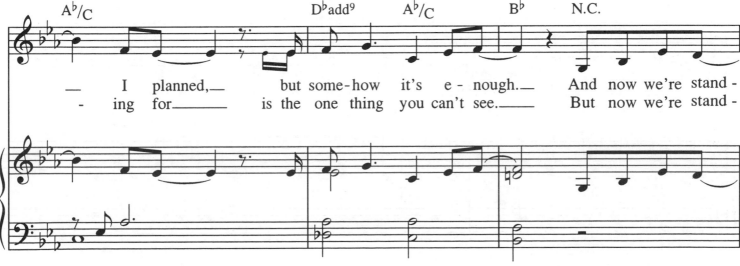

I planned,  but some-how it's e - nough.  And now we're stand-
- ing for  is the one thing you can't see.  But now we're stand-

- ing face to face. }
- ing face to face. }

Is-n't this world a cra - -zy place?

Just when I thought our chance had passed, you go and save

**1.2.**

— the best for last.

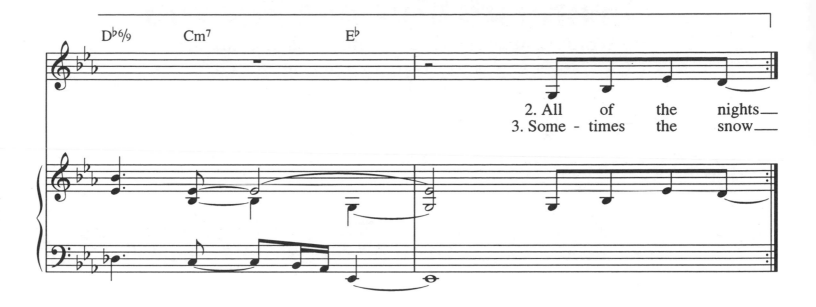

2. All of the nights___
3. Some - times the snow___

**CODA**

**rit.**

You went and saved___ the best___ for last.___

**a tempo**  **rall.**

Yeah.___

# Saving All My Love For You

### Words & Music by Gerry Goffin & Michael Masser

A few sto-len mo-ments is all that we share.
not ver-y eas-y liv-ing all a-lone. My

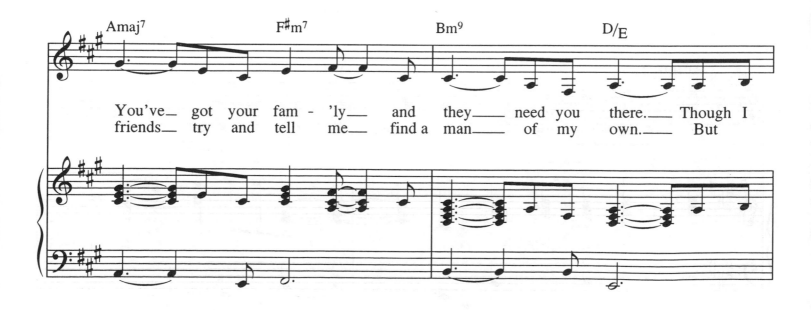

You've got your fam-'ly and they need you there. Though I
friends try and tell me find a man of my own. But

try\_\_\_ to re - sist,\_\_\_ be -ing last\_\_\_ on your list, but
each\_\_\_ time I try,\_\_\_ I just break\_\_\_ down and cry, 'cause I'd

no oth - er man's\_\_\_ gon - na do.\_\_\_ So I'm
rath - er be home\_\_\_ feel -in' blue.\_\_\_

sav - ing all my love for you.\_\_\_

It's_____

You used to tell__ me__ we'd

run a-way to-geth-er;__

love gives you the right__ to be free._____ You

said:____ "Be pa - tient,__ just wait a lit - tle long-er,"____ But

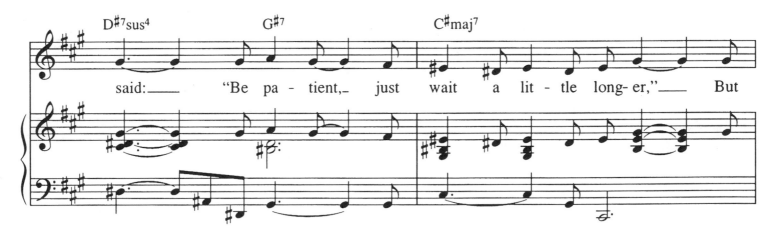

that's just__ an old fan - ta - sy._____ I've got__ to get read- y,__ just a

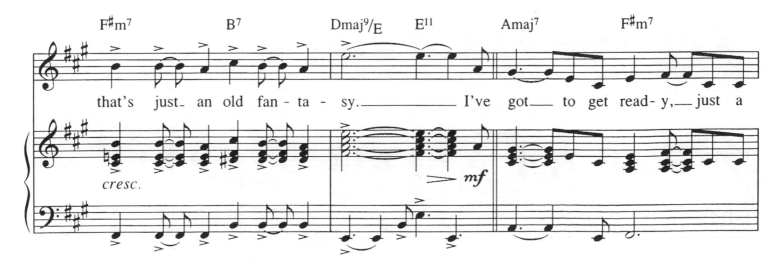

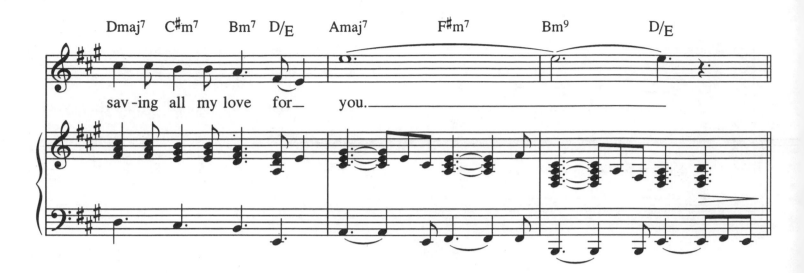

sav-ing all my love for— you._____

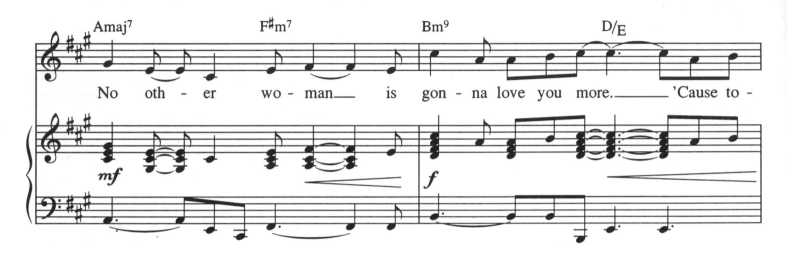

No oth-er wo-man— is gon-na love you more.____ 'Cause to-

night__ is the night____ that I'm feel - -ing all right.____ We'll be

mak-ing love the whole__ night__ through;_____ so I'm

sav-ing all my love, yes I'm sav-ing all my lov-ing,— yes I'm

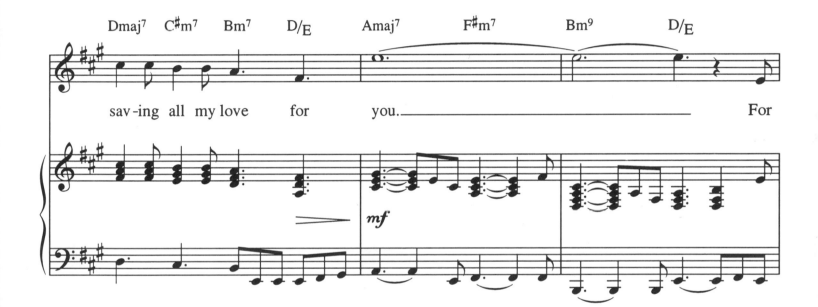

sav-ing all my love for you._____ For

you._____

# Show Me Heaven

### Words & Music by Maria McKee, Jay Rifkin & Eric Rackin

**Moderately**

1. There you go, flash-ing fe - ver from your eyes.
(Verse 2 see block lyric)

Hey babe,— come ov - er here— and shut down tight.—

I'm not de-ny - ing we're fly-ing a-bove— it all,—

hold my hand— don't let me fall— you've such a-ma - zing

grace, I've ne -ver felt this way.— Oh,—

*cresc.* *f*

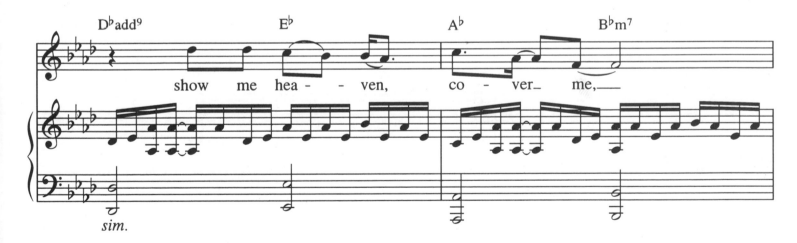

show me hea - - ven, co - ver— me,—

*sim.*

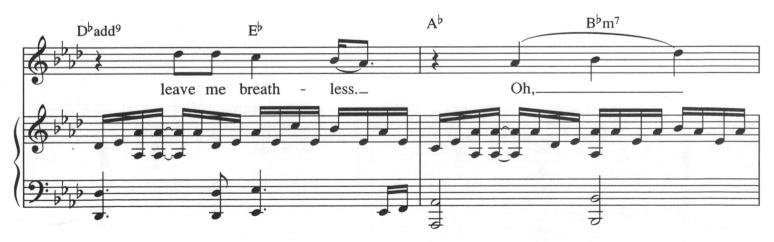

leave me breath - less.— Oh,—

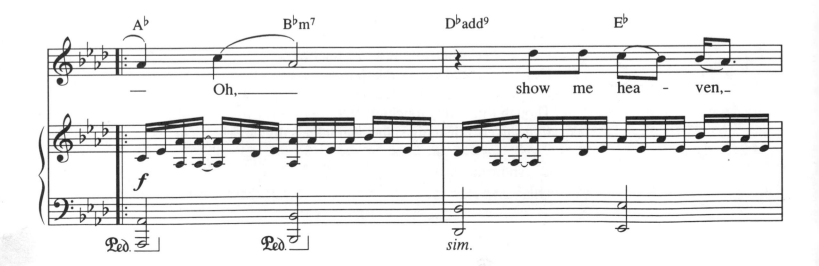

*Verse 2:*

Here I go, I'm shaking just like the breeze.
Hey babe, I need your hand to steady me.
I'm not denying I'm frightened as much as you.
Though I'm barely touching you,
I've shivers down my spine, and it feels divine.

Oh, show me heaven, *etc.*

# Someone To Watch Over Me

## Music & Lyrics by George Gershwin & Ira Gershwin

1. There's a some-bo-dy I'm long-ing to see: I hope that he turns out to be
2. I'm a lit-tle lamb who's lost in the wood; I know I could al-ways be good

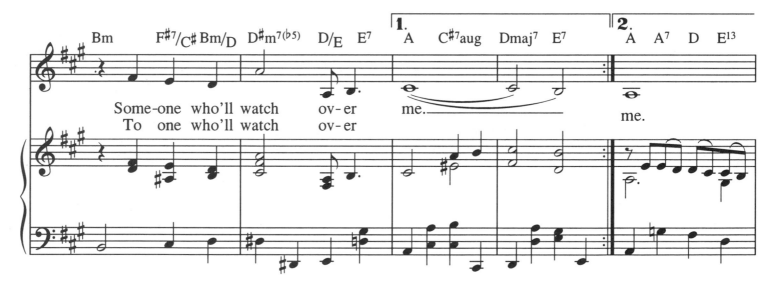

Some-one who'll watch ov-er me.
To one who'll watch ov-er me.

Al-though he may not be the man some girls think of as

hand-some, To my heart he car-ries the key.

Won't you tell him please to put on some speed, Fol-low my lead; oh, how I need

*To Coda*

Some-one to watch ov-er me.

*D.S. al Coda*

Al-though he

**CODA**
*rit.*

watch ov - er me.

# Tell Me It's Not True

## Words & Music by Willy Russell

**Rather slow**

1. Tell me it's not
*(Verse 2 see block lyric)*

true. Say it's just a sto - ry Some-thing in the news.

Tell me it's not true, though it's here be -

-fore_____ me.    Say it's just a dream,    say it's just a scene___

from an old mo -vie of    years__ a - go;    from an old mo -vie of

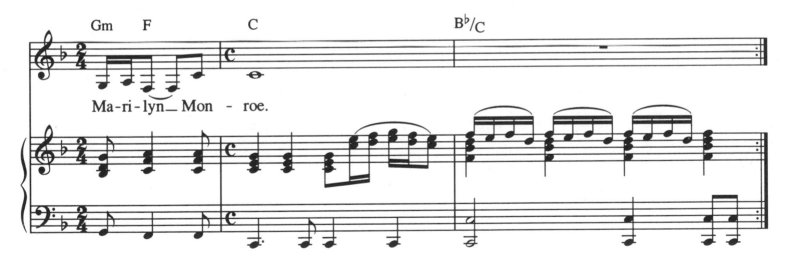

Ma -ri -lyn__ Mon - roe.

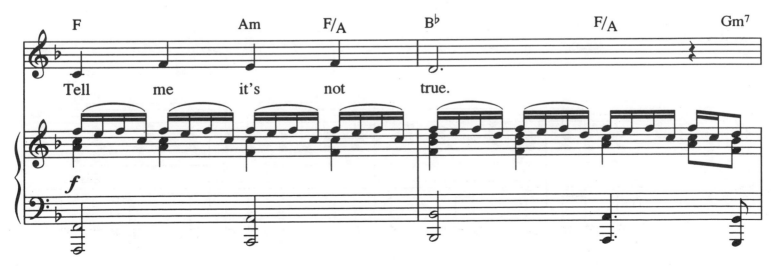

Tell    me    it's    not    true.

Say I on- ly dreamed_____ it. And

morn - ing will come soon. Tell me it's not

true. Say you did- n't

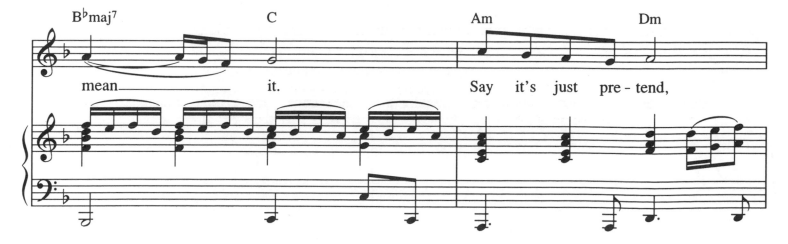

mean_____ it. Say it's just pre - tend,

**Verse 2:**
Say it's just some clowns,
Two players in the limelight.
And bring the curtain down.
Say it's just two clowns
Who couldn't get their lines right.
Say it's just a show on the radio
That we can turn over and start again;
We can turn over, it's only a game.

139

# That Ole Devil Called Love

## Words & Music by Doris Fisher & Allan Roberts

**Lazy swing**

It's that old dev-il called love a-gain. Gets be-hind me and keeps giv-ing me that shove a-gain. Put-ting rain in my eyes, tears in my dreams, and rocks in my heart. It's that sly old son-of-a-

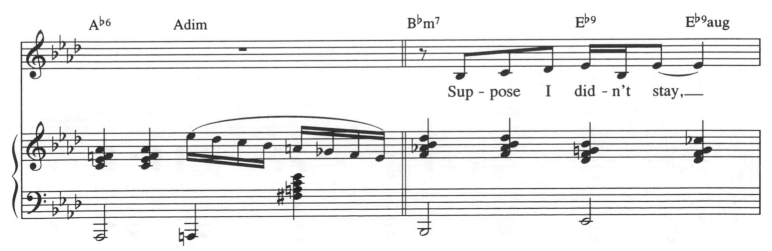

ran a - way,____ would-n't play,____ that de - vil what a po - tion he would

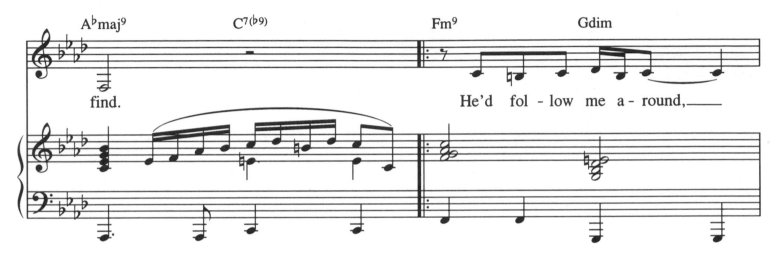

find. He'd fol - low me a - round,____

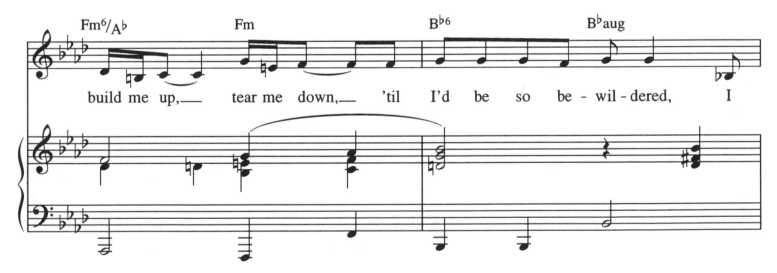

build me up,____ tear me down,____ 'til I'd be so be - wil - dered, I

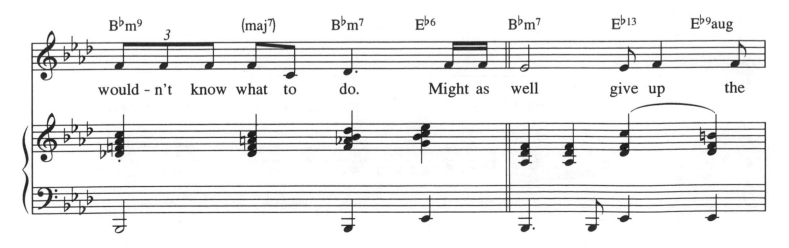

would-n't know what to do. Might as well give up the

fight a - gain.___ I know darn well he'll con - vince me that he's

right a - gain. When he sings that si - ren song,

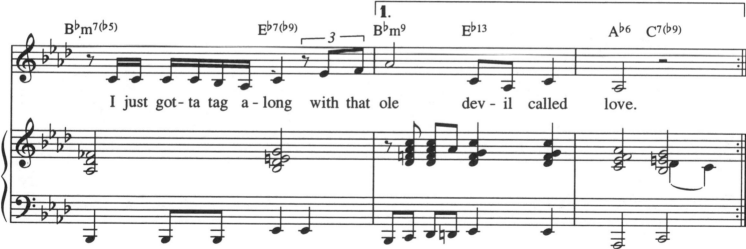

**1.**

I just got - ta tag a - long with that ole dev - il called love.

**2.**

ole dev - il called love, with that ole dev - il called love.___

# What I Did For Love

Words by Edward Kleban
Music by Marvin Hamlisch

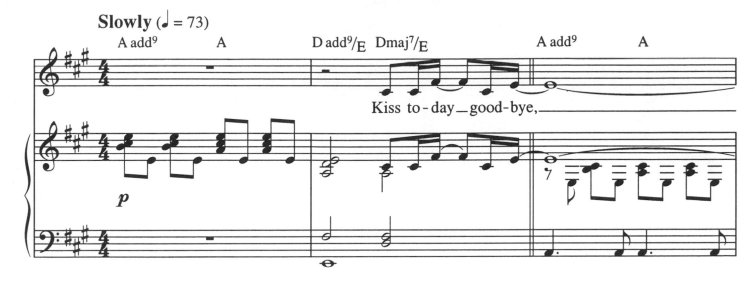

Kiss to-day good-bye,

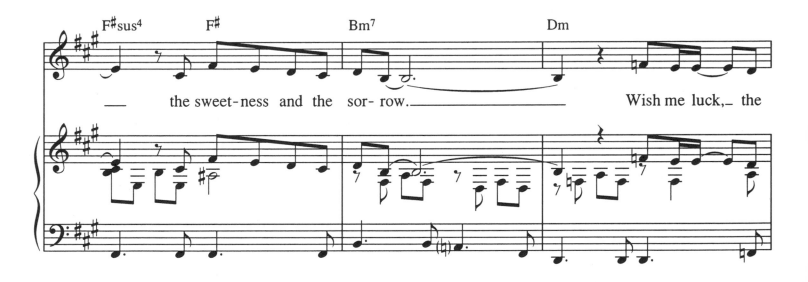

the sweet-ness and the sor-row. Wish me luck, the

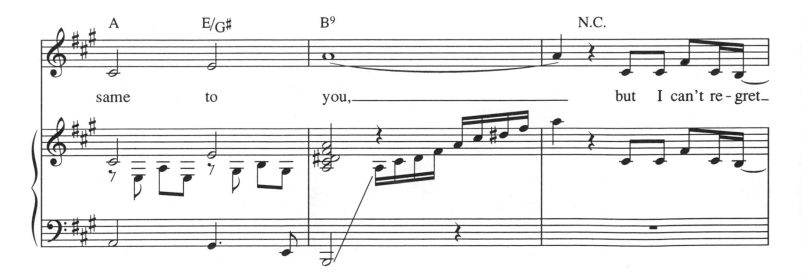

same to you, but I can't re-gret

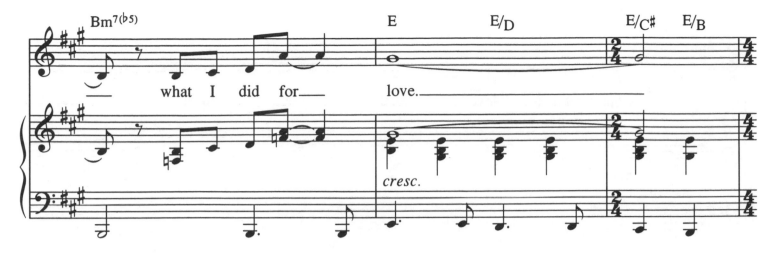

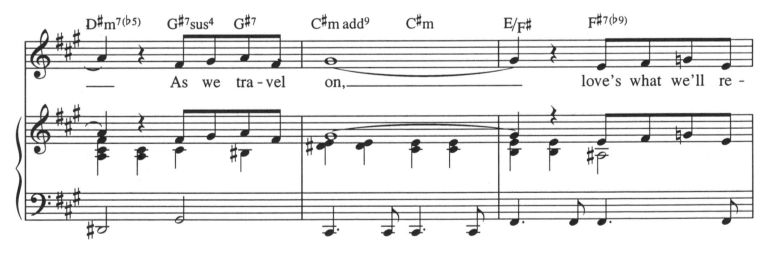

and point me t'ward to-mor-row. _____ We did what_ we had_

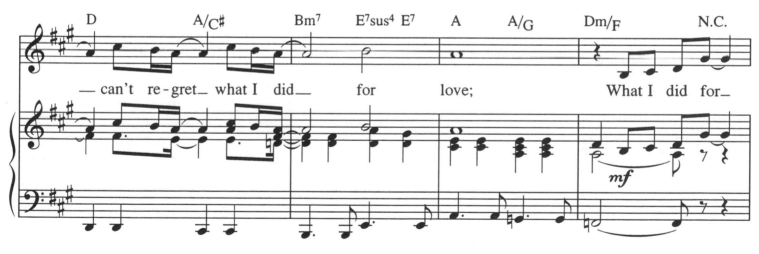

to do. _____ Won't for-get,_

—can't re-gret_ what I did_ for love; What I did for_

love, What I did for_ love. _____

# Someone Else's Story

## Words & Music by Benny Andersson, Tim Rice & Bjorn Ulvaeus

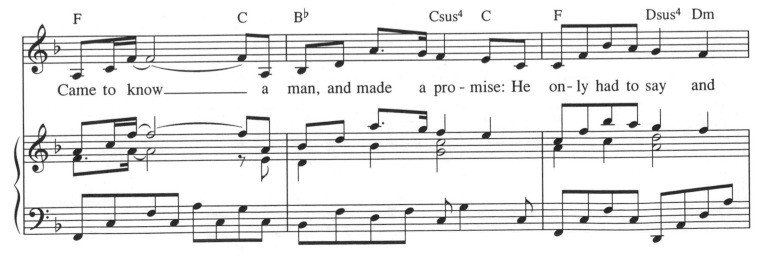

1. Long a-go, in
(Verse 2 see block lyric)

1st time play arpegg.
2nd time play melody

some-one el-se's life-time, Some-one with my name,—who looks— a lot— like me,—

Came to know— a man, and made a pro-mise: He on-ly had to say and

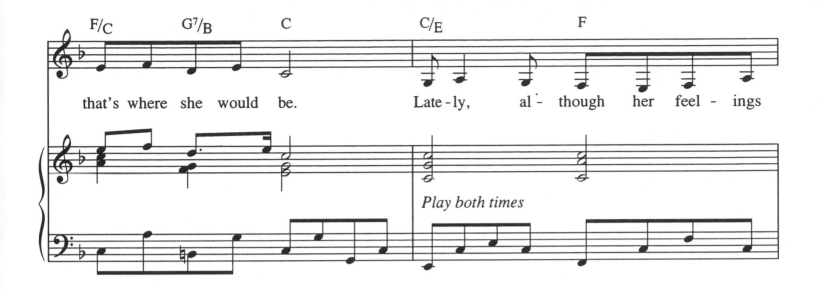

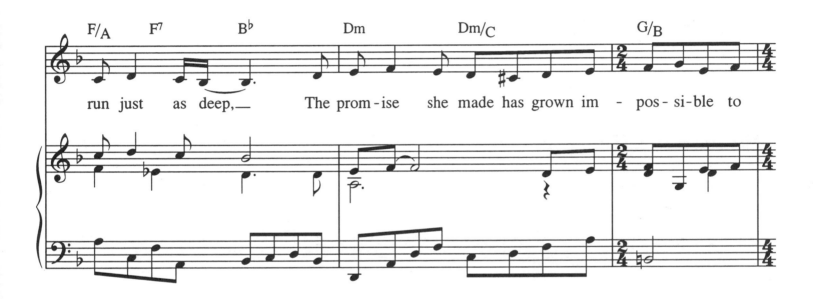

All ve-ry well to say "You fool, it's now or nev - er!". I could be choos - ing

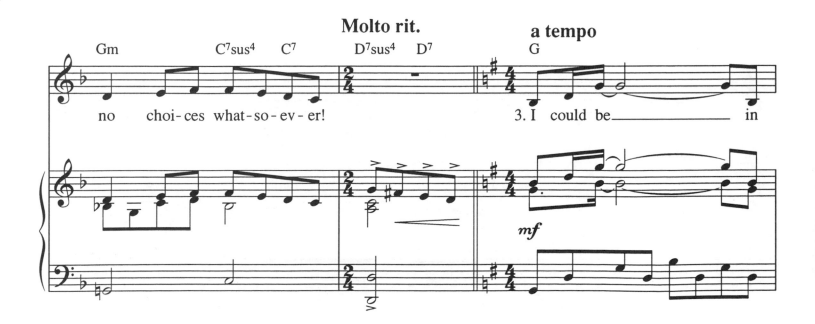

no choi-ces what-so-ev - er! 3. I could be_____ in

some-one el-se's sto - ry, In some-one el-se's life,___ and he___ could be in mine.___

I don't see___ a rea-son to be lone-ly; I should take my chan - ces

fur-ther down the line. And if that girl I knew should ask my ad-vice, Oh

I would-n't he-si-tate, she need-n't ask me twice._____ "Go now!" I'd

tell her that for free. Trou-ble is,— the girl— is me.— The

**poco rit.**

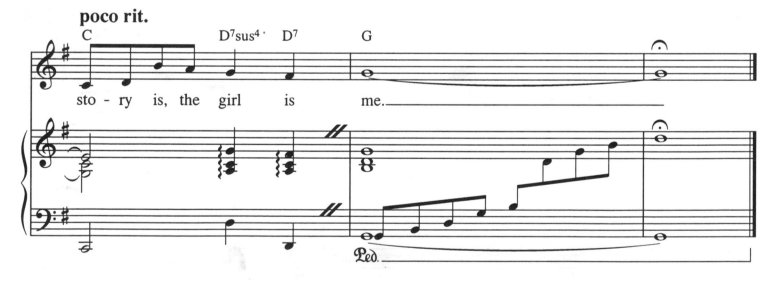

sto-ry is, the girl is me._____

*Verse 2*

In a way, it's someone else's story;
I don't see myself as taking part at all.
Yesterday, a girl that I was fond of
Finally could see the writing on the wall.
Sadly, she realized she'd left him behind;
And, sadder than that, she knew
She wouldn't even mind.
And though there's nothing left to say,
Would he listen if I stay?

# The Wind Beneath My Wings

### Words & Music by Jeff Silbar & Larry Henley

You were con - tent___ to let me shine.___

You al - ways walked___ a step be - hind.___

to hide the pain.___ Did you ev - er know___

___ that you're my he - ro, And ev - 'ry - thing I___

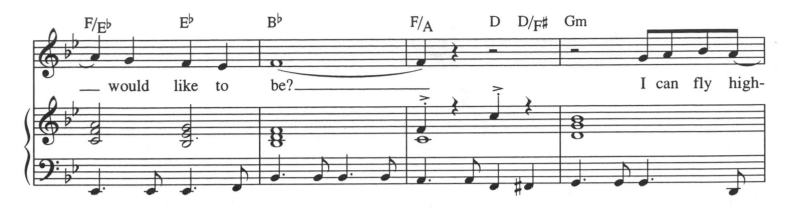

_\_\_ would like to be?_____ I can fly high-_

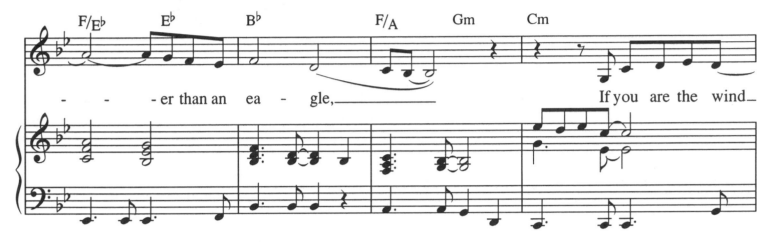

_\- - - er than an ea - gle,_____ If you are the wind\__

To ⊕ Coda

D.%  (as 2nd time) al Coda

_\_ be-neath my wings._____

⊕ **CODA**

_wings._____ Did I ev-er tell\_\_ you you're my\_\__

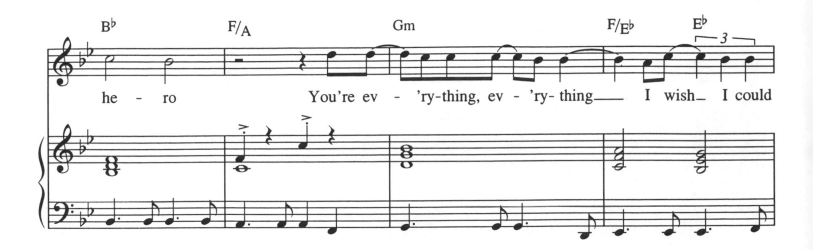

he - ro        You're ev - 'ry-thing, ev - 'ry-thing___ I wish___ I could

be.___        Oh,   and I_____ I can fly high - - - er than an

ea - - gle,_____   If you are the wind___ be-neath my

wings;_____   If you  are  the  wind___

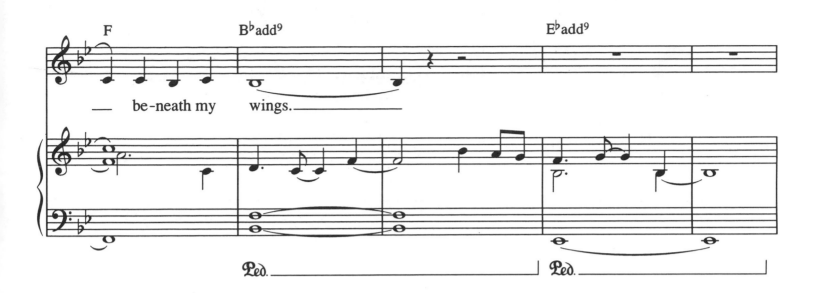

be-neath my wings.

Thank God for you,_ the wind be-neath_ my wings.

*Verse 2*
So I was the one with all the glory,
While you were the one with all the strain;
A beautiful face without a name,
A beautiful smile to hide the pain.
Did you ever know, etc.

*Verse 3*
It might have appeared to go unnoticed,
But I've got it all here in my heart.
I want you to know I know the truth:
I would be nothing without you.
Did you ever know, etc.

# The Winner Takes It All

## Words & Music by Benny Andersson & Bjorn Ulvaeus

**Rhythmically**

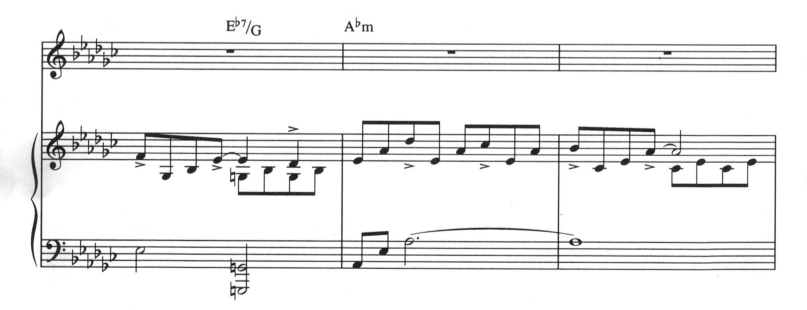

1. I don't wan-na

talk
2. arms

*(Verses 3 & 4 see block lyric)*

a - bout things we've gone through,
think - ing I be - longed there,

though it's hurt - ing me,
I fi - gured it made sense,

now it's his - to-
build-ing me a

ry.
fence,

I've played all my cards
build - ing me a home,

and that's what you've done too,
think - ing I'd be strong there,

no - thing more to
but I was a

say,
fool,

no more ace to play.
play-ing by the rules.

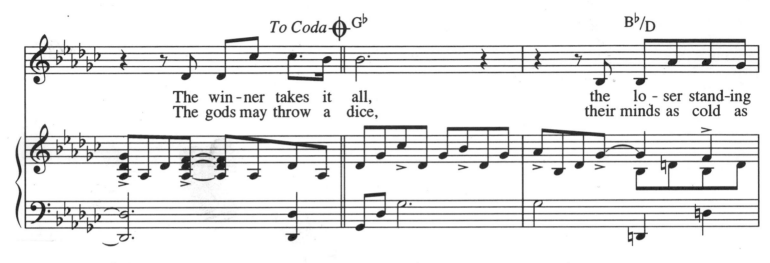

*To Coda* ⊕ G♭

The win-ner takes it all,
The gods may throw a dice,

the lo-ser stand-ing
their minds as cold as

small
ice,

be-side the vic-to-ry,
and some-one way down here

_ that's_ her des-ti- ny.
_ lo - ses some-one dear.

2. I was in your

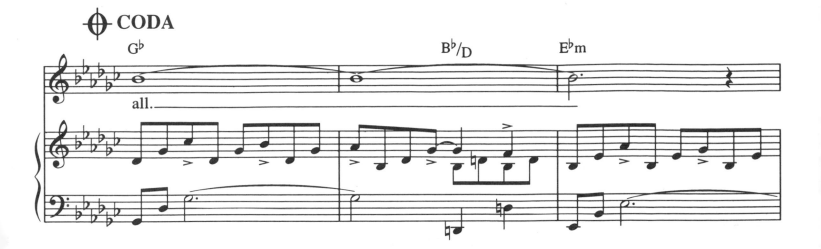

**⊕ CODA**

The win-ner takes it all.

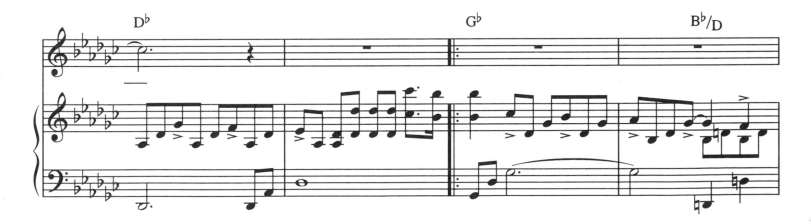

*Verse 3:*

But tell me, does she kiss like I used to kiss you,
Does it feel the same when she calls your name?
Somewhere deep inside,
You must know I miss you,
But what can I say,
Rules must be obeyed.
The judges will decide the likes of me abide,
Spectators of the show always staying low.

*Verse 4:*

I don't wanna talk
If it makes you feel sad
And I understand you've come to shake my hand.
I apologise if it makes you feel bad
Seeing me so tense,
No self-confidence.
The winner takes it all.
The winner takes it all.

# Wishing You Were Somehow Here Again

### Music by Andrew Lloyd Webber
### Lyrics by Charles Hart. Additional lyrics by Richard Stilgoe

poco rit.　　　a tempo

some-how you would be here.　　　Wish-ing I could hear your

voice a-gain,　　　know-ing that I nev-er would,　　　dream-ing of you　won't

help me to do　　　all that you dreamed　I could.

Pass-ing bells　and sculp-ted an-gels, cold and mo-nu-men-tal,

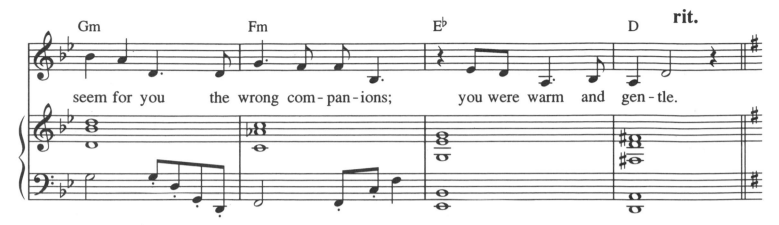

seem for you    the wrong com - pan - ions;     you were warm   and   gen - tle.

**poco meno mosso**

**accel.**

Too ma - ny years,     fight - ing back tears,     why can't the past    just

*cresc.*

**rit.**     **maestoso**

die?      Wish - ing you were some - how   here a - gain,

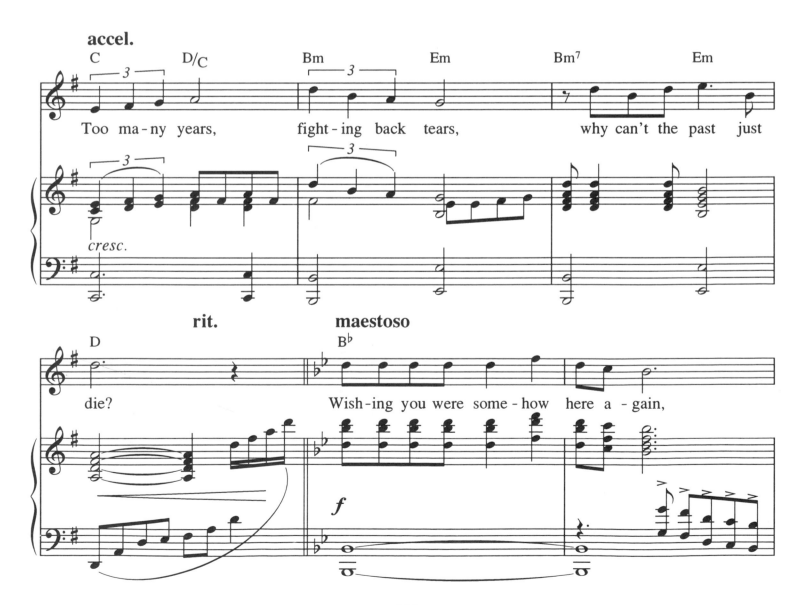

know-ing we must say good - bye.   Try   to   for -give,

teach   me   to   love,   give me the strength to   try.   No more

me-mo-ries,   no   more   si - lent tears, no more gaz -ing a - cross the

wast - ed   years.   Help me say   good - bye!

167

# You Can Always Count On Me

Music by Cy Coleman
Words by David Zippel

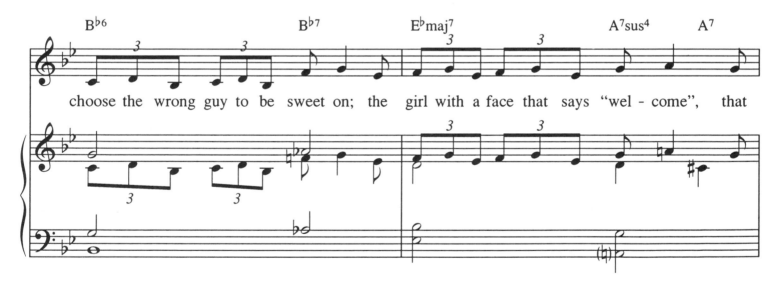

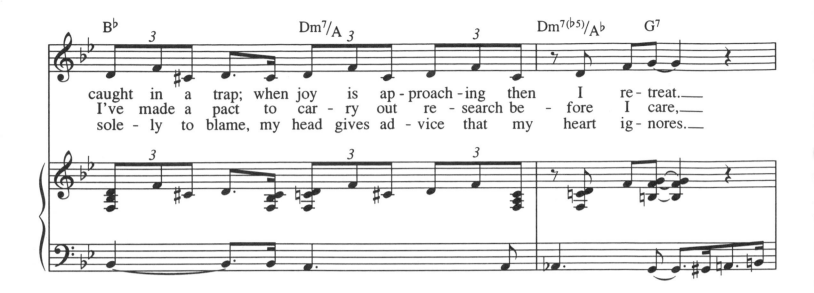

caught in a trap; when joy is ap - proach - ing then I re - treat.___
I've made a pact to car - ry out re - search be - fore I care,___
sole - ly to blame, my head gives ad - vice that my heart ig - nores.___

I'm at home with mis - er - y.___          I've
men don't give a war - ran - ty.___        One
I'm my on - ly en - e - my.___             I

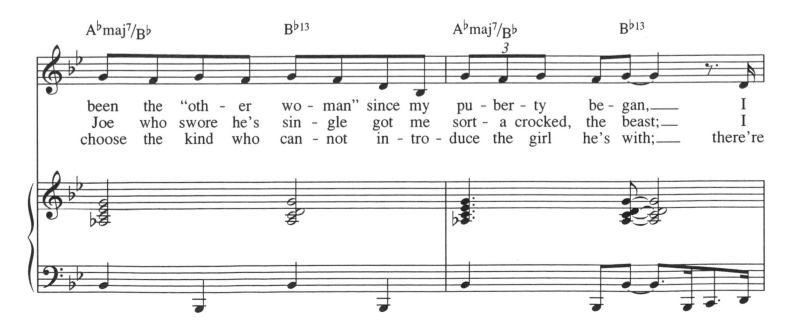

been the "oth - er wo - man" since my pu - ber - ty be - gan,___   I
Joe who swore he's sin - gle got me sort - a crocked, the beast;___   I
choose the kind who can - not in - tro - duce the girl he's with;___   there're

crashed the jun-ior prom and met the on-ly __ mar-ried man. __ I'm
woke up on-ly slight-ly shocked that I'd de-frocked a priest. __ Or
lots of smirk-ing mo-tel clerks who call me __ Miss-us Smith, __ but

al-ways on top for ro-mance or choc-'late that's bit-ter - sweet. __
else I at-tract the guys who are long-ing to do my hair. __
I've made a name with ho-tel de-tect-ives who break down doors. __

*To Coda*

You can al-ways count on me. __ A __
You can al-ways count on me. __ I

**1.**

**2.**

# You Must Love Me

## Music by Andrew Lloyd Webber
## Lyrics by Tim Rice

**Moderately**

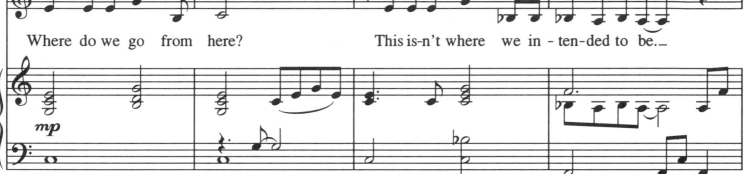

Where do we go from here? This is-n't where we in-ten-ded to be._

We had it all,_ you be-lieved_ in me,_ I be-lieved_ in you.

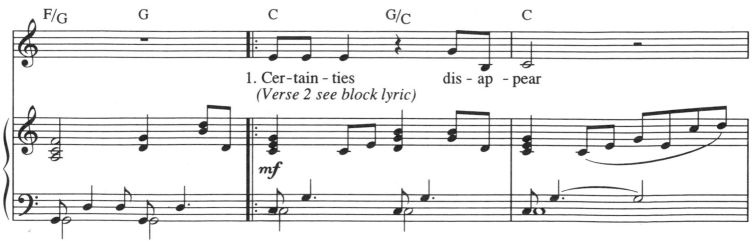

1. Cer-tain-ties     dis-ap-pear
(Verse 2 see block lyric)

what do we do___ for our dream to sur-vive, how do we keep___ all our

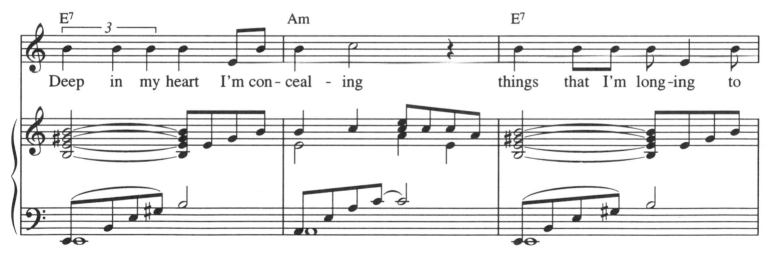

pas-sions a - live___ as we used to do?___

Deep in my heart I'm con - ceal - ing things that I'm long-ing to

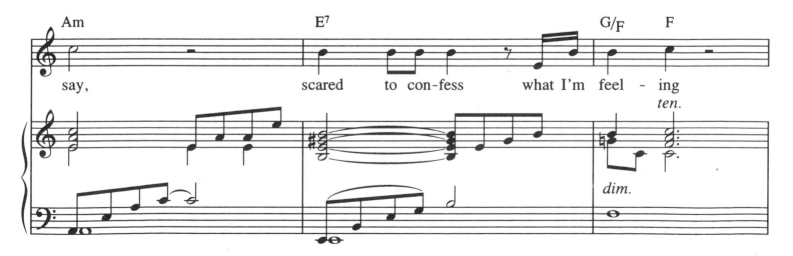

say, scared to con-fess what I'm feel - ing

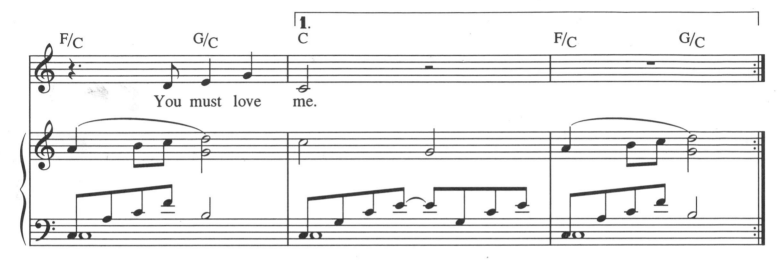

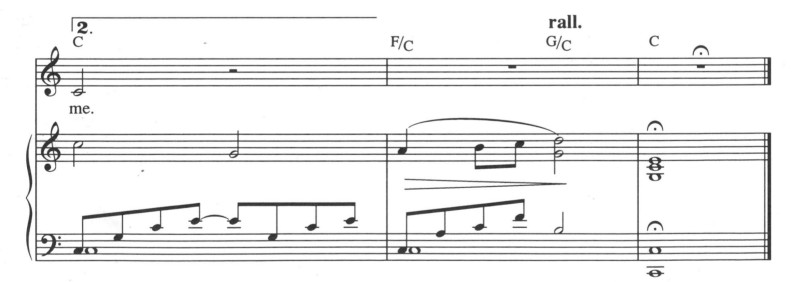

*Verse 2:*
Why are you at my side?
How can I be any use to you now?
Give me a chance and I'll let you see how
Nothing has changed.
Deep in my heart I'm concealing
Things that I'm longing to say,
Scared to confess what I'm feeling
Frightened you'll slip away,
You must love me.

Printed in Malta by Progress Press Co. Ltd.    1/06(57235)